Beauty Therapy Science

R. A. Bembridge, B.Sc.

Longman Scientific & Technical
Longman Group UK Limited,
Longman House, Burnt Mill, Harlow,
Essex CM20 2JE, England
and Associated Companies throughout the world.

First published 1988
Third impression 1991

British Library Cataloguing in Publication Data
Bembridge, R. A.
   Beauty therapy science.
   1. Beauty culture——Miscellanea
   2. Science
   I. Title
   502′.46467   TT957

ISBN 0-582-46819-1

Set in 10/11pt Times Comp/Edit 6400

Printed in Malaysia
by Chee Leong Press Sdn. Bhd.,
Ipoh, Perak Darul Ridzuan

Contents

Part 3   The ingredients of cosmetics

Part 4   Salon treatments

Preface

This book has been written to provide a text for students studying for a number of beauty therapy examinations including City and Guilds of London Institute (304-1), the International Health and Beauty Council Beauty Specialists Diploma and International Beauty Diploma, and those of the British Association of Beauty Therapists and Cosmetologists. It will also form introductory reading for students taking the new BTEC National Diploma in Beauty Therapy.

The science covered concentrates on the physics and chemistry behind the activities and treatments taking place in the modern salon and endeavours to give a concise explanation for the inclusion of the various ingredients that make up the cosmetics in use today. To a large extent, no previous knowledge of the science involved has been assumed and explanations of the sometimes complex concepts behind the work of the therapist have been given in a manner to make them understandable to a student whose interests lie in the salon rather than in the laboratory.

A selection of questions appears at the end of each chapter which will provide the student with an opportunity to describe and explain the subject matter in her own words, and to appreciate the relationships between topics covered therein. Two appendices should prove of value when revision time arrives, and when an easily-obtained answer to a query is required.

I would like to record here my thanks to my former colleagues in the Science Division and the Hair and Beauty Division of North Warwickshire College of Technology and Art who first encouraged me to write this book and then continued to assist me with much help and advice. My thanks also go to my wife for her patience, understanding and support during the period when creating this book formed such a major part of my daily life.

Part 1
The beauty salon

Chapter 1

Salon heating

It is important that when a client enters a beauty salon she enters a place where an atmosphere of relaxation prevails. She will not expect to be asked to perform any energy-consuming activities. During any treatment which she undergoes her therapist will make every effort to see that she is placed in a comfortable position. For the client therefore it will be important that the temperature of the salon shall be warm enough to suit such restful conditions.

From the therapist's point of view however the salon can be a place where she may be involved in very energetic activity. When carrying out a body massage, for example, the amount of reserve energy converted to heat can be considerable. Too warm a salon will not be in the interests of the salon staff.

Salon temperature

The conflict between the comfort of clients and satisfactory working conditions for the therapists when selecting and achieving a suitable salon temperature is difficult to resolve, but 20°C should be regarded as a minimum value with higher values up to 25°C obtained if possible. The therapist must allow for these higher values in choosing the amount of clothing worn while working.

The outside temperature in the British Isles is below 20°C for most of the year so it will be necessary for the salon to have some form of heating, but in order to understand and compare the methods available a knowledge of how heat travels is required.

Methods of heat travel

The heat energy possessed by an object is now considered to be the energy of movement of the particles (or molecules) from which it is made. A rise in temperature means that the motions of the molecules have become more agitated. Heat energy will move naturally from places at high temperature to places at lower temperatures and there are several ways in which this can occur.

1. Conduction

This is the way in which heat energy travels through solids. Any extra energy received by one molecule from a heat source causes it to become more agitated, but because molecules of a solid are close together those surrounding the agitated molecule are jostled about more and this effect spreads throughout the whole object (see Fig. 1.1).

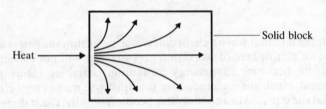

Fig. 1.1 Movement of heat by conduction

The best heat conductors are solid metals like copper and aluminium. Non-metallic solids like glass, wood and asbestos are much poorer conductors and are often used as *insulators*. Liquids and gases are not very good conductors as their molecules are further apart. Use is often made of this fact when porous or open-weave materials are chosen for insulation such as glass fibre matting in lofts and woollen knitted garments. It is the air trapped in small spaces within such materials that helps to make them such good retainers of heat.

Experiment 1.1   To show water is a poor conductor of heat
Take a glass boiling tube and fill it with water to about two-thirds capacity. Hold the sealed end of the tube in the hand and incline the tube as shown in Fig. 1.2 Apply a small gas flame to the tube just below the

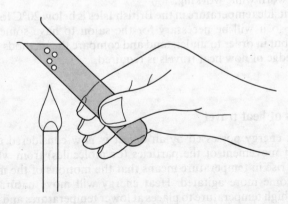

Fig. 1.2 Water a poor heat conductor

water level. It will be possible to continue to hold the tube as shown even when the water at the top is boiling. Heat is not easily conducted down to the hand.

2. Convection
Because liquid and gas (or vapour) molecules are further apart than the molecules of a solid they are also able to move about freely from place to place within the space occupied by the liquid or gas. This fact makes it possible for a second method of heat travel in liquids and gases known as *convection*. When a molecule receives heat energy from a heat source it can move away from the source, taking the extra energy with it.

This is the method employed for most heating systems used to maintain the temperature of the salon. The air near the heat source expands as most substances do when the temperature rises. This lowers the air density in that region and this lighter air then floats upwards to the ceiling just as an air bubble in water will rise to the surface of the water. The space left by the heated salon air will be filled by cooler, denser air falling downwards. Thus a *convection current* will be set up (see Fig. 1.3) and, as a result, the temperature of the salon air will gradually rise. Use of convection in a liquid is described in Chapter 3.

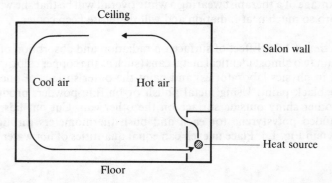

Ceiling

Salon wall

Cool air   Hot air

Heat source

Floor

Fig. 1.3 Convection current in salon air

3. Radiation
The rapid agitations of the particles in the surface of a hot solid object have an influence on conditions in the space surrounding the object. This can be compared with the movement of the surface of a puddle caused by a falling raindrop, which then spreads outwards in the form of water waves (see Ch. 19). Heat waves radiate outwards from the surface of the hot object and carry heat energy with them. This gives a third method of heat travel called *radiation* which does not require molecules to carry it along. It is the only method possible in empty space. Heat from the sun reaches the earth's atmosphere by this method. If a radiant

heat lamp has a vacuum inside the bulb, the heat from the filament will travel to the glass of the bulb by radiation only.

These waves emanating from hot objects are also known as *infra-red waves* (see Ch. 19). All objects at a higher temperature than their surroundings will lose heat by this method but if they are in contact with air, as in the salon, there will also be a loss by convection. The higher the temperature of an object, the greater is the proportion of heat lost by radiation compared with that lost by convection. A radiant electric fire will distribute most of its heat by radiation waves because of the high temperature of the element wire. On the other hand, the human body at 37°C loses about 25 per cent of its heat to the surroundings by conduction and convection as against 43 per cent by radiation. Most of the remaining heat loss is by the method described in the next section.

Apart from temperature, the condition of the surface of the hot object will also determine the ease with which heat radiation escapes from it (see Expt. 1.2). *Dull black* surfaces are the *best* radiators, *shiny bright* surfaces are the *poorest* radiators of heat. Heat radiation will travel across the salon and will only give up its energy when it reaches a surface capable of absorbing its waves. When this happens the surface concerned will get warmer. *Dull black* surfaces are the *best* absorbers, *shiny bright* surfaces are the *poorest* absorbers of radiant heat. One advantage of a therapist wearing a white overall will be that she will not absorb so much heat radiation and will therefore keep cooler.

Experiment 1.2   Effect of surface on radiation and absorbtion of heat
Obtain two almost identical metal cans (such as the copper calorimeters used in physics laboratories) and paint the outer surface of one with matt black paint. Using metal polish or buffing powder, produce a smoother shiny outside surface on the other can. Cut out lids from expanded polystyrene for each and push thermometers through as shown in Fig. 1.4. Place in each can equal quantitiés of hot water from

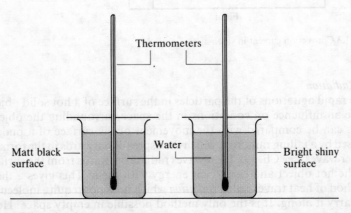

Fig. 1.4 Effect of surface on heat radiation

an electric kettle and note the temperatures of the water in the cans. Leave the cans to stand in the same part of the room and on the same surface. Read the temperatures at regular intervals and note which can cools the most rapidly.

Now empty the cans and place them at the same distance (5 to 10 cm) from a radiant electric bowl fire element. Add the same quantity of tap water at the same temperature to each can and then switch on the radiator. Check the temperature of the water at regular intervals to find out which surface is the best absorber.

Cooling by evaporation

When a liquid changes to a vapour it requires an additional quantity of heat energy to do so. This is because the molecules of a liquid are packed close together and are, therefore, able to exert mutual attractions for each other. Any molecule that is to escape from the liquid and become part of a vapour needs to be travelling at high speed when it reaches the surface to overcome the attraction of the molecules left behind. To reach this high speed, energy is required and is supplied in the form of heat. Since no rise in temperature is produced by this additional energy we call it *latent heat*, which means hidden heat.

This latent heat must be obtained from somewhere and the nearest source is the surface from which the liquid is evaporating. This causes a cooling effect on the surface and is particularly noticeable if the liquid evaporating does so rapidly. Such a liquid is said to be *volatile*.

The effect is noticed if perfume or eau de cologne is spilled on the skin and may be used purposely to cool a person's forehead during illness. Its most important biological application is *perspiration*, when the evaporating sweat helps to remove heat from the body, thus assisting in the control of body temperature.

Experiment 1.3 Cooling by evaporation

Clamp a thermometer in a stand and surround its bulb with a piece of cotton wool held on with a rubber band. Note the temperature reading and then soak the cotton wool in eau de cologne or toilet water and notice how the evaporation of the liquid has a cooling effect on the thermometer bulb.

Central heating

A true central heating system for a salon will have heat produced at some central point, and this heat will then be conveyed as hot water or as hot air to different parts of the premises.

The more common system is that which contains a *boiler* where water is heated and then circulated by means of *pipes* to *radiators* from which heat is given out by both radiation and convection. The cooled water then returns to the boiler. In modern systems this circulation is brought about by an electrically-driven *pump*. This means that, regardless of the fuel used to heat the boiler, a power-cut can effectively shut off the heating of the salon. The water in the system must be kept topped-up by including a *header tank* connected via a ball-valve to the water mains.

A salon owner who decides to install this sytem of central heating does not necessarily have to find floor space for a boiler as wall-mounted boilers and master radiators that also act as boilers are now available. The system can also be designed to supply hot water for wash-basins and showers by including a special storage tank (see Ch. 3).

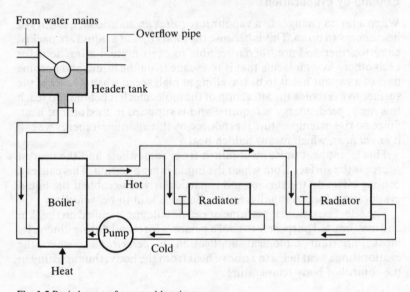

Fig. 1.5 Basic layout of a central heating system

The warm-air system will have a central *air heater* which is connected by *ducts* in the walls and ceiling to *grilles* which open into the rooms to be heated. Some form of *fan* will be required to drive the air along the ducting.

Both systems will have a *thermostat* to control the amount of fuel consumed and there will usually be a *time-switch* to switch the boiler or heater on and off at pre-selected times. Any fuel can be chosen to generate the heat when the system is first installed, but to change later would normally involve modifications or the purchase of a new boiler or air-heater. Natural gas or electricity are attractive fuels since, unlike oil or solid fuel, storage on the premises is not required, but the cost of fuel will play a large part in choosing which to use. Ash disposal is also a complication with solid fuel.

Storage and underfloor heating

These methods make use of cheaper off-peak electricity. For a number of hours during the night electric current flows through the heating elements. These are surrounded by a mass of material which is capable of storing heat while it is being generated by the current. This material often takes the form of special bricks inside *storage heaters* . As it is a relatively poor conductor, heat escapes from it only slowly and this continues throughout the day-time when no current is flowing through the element.

A time clock set by the electricity supplier will switch the current on and off automatically. The electrical energy consumed can be offered at a cheaper rate because it will be taken from the National Grid when consumption by day-time users is absent.

Modern storage heaters can now be fastened to the wall, leaving the floor clear underneath. The volume of space they would occupy in a salon is quite small. They are usually fitted with an input control and an output control. The former would be set by the salon staff after taking into account the forecast outside temperature for the following day and the desired inside temperature. It can take the form of a bimetal switch which is temperature-sensitive and operates in the manner described later in this chapter. Most of the stored heat is radiated from the casing during the day-time. Some heat, however, is emitted through a grill at the top of the heater, and is regulated by the output control. This consists of a shutter which on some models is opened and shut manually, while others have a bimetal temperature sensor which opens the shutter when the temperature of the heater falls to a value determined by the consumer's setting of the control. This latter type of control can be set to emit most of its heat boost during the day, i.e. while the salon is in use.

Underfloor heating is a method which uses the solid ground floor of a building as a massive storage heater. The electrical heating elements must be set in the floor when the building is constructed. Like storage heaters, electrical energy is converted into heat during the night and this gradually escapes during the day-time, mostly by means of convection currents in the air of the salon. The two main disadvantages of this system are

1. It cannot be installed in an existing building.
2. The floor on which the salon staff will be spending much of the day standing tends to be the warmest part of the salon and this can result in foot problems.

Convector heaters

Unlike previous systems of heating described, convector heaters are individual units and are often portable, thus allowing repositioning in different locations as required. The heat can be generated by using natural gas (not portable), bottle gas (propane or butane), paraffin oil or electricity. Their mode of action is shown in Fig. 1.3 where they take in cool air through a lower grille and give out warm air through a higher grille. The temperature of the outside case of the heater is much lower than that of the inside heat source, which usually means they are safe to touch – but care must be taken not to cover the heat outlet with towels, etc. as this will result in a dangerous rise in the heater temperature.

Radiant heaters

This type of heater has a high temperature source exposed to the room and gives out the majority of its heat in the form of radiation. Gas and electric fires are the types most likely to find use in a beauty salon if at all, but because of the directional nature of heat radiation they tend to provide heat in certain parts rather than giving all-round warmth (see Fig. 1.6). Great care must be taken in positioning radiant heaters and their heat source must be surrounded by a guard to reduce the risk of fire. The therapist is more likely to use this form of heating as part of treatment when she uses radiant heat or infra-red lamps, rather than as a means of raising the salon temperature.

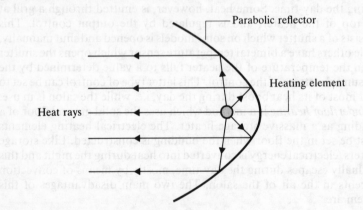

Fig. 1.6 Directional nature of a radiant heater

The thermostat

Most of the heating systems installed in salons will require a form of automatic regulator which will control the amount of heat produced, depending on the temperature desired in the salon. Saunas, showers, facial steamers, wax heaters and other equipment used by the therapist will also require temperature control. Such a device is called a *thermostat* and the majority of these operate by including a *bimetal strip* (see Fig. 1.7).

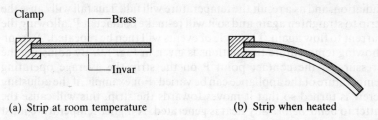

(a) Strip at room temperature   (b) Strip when heated

Fig. 1.7 Operation of a bimetal strip

A bimetal strip is made from two layers of different metals fixed rigidly together, one of which expands considerably more than the other on heating. Brass and an alloy called invar are often chosen since the brass in the strip expands twenty times as much as the invar for the same temperature rise. These different expanding properties can only be accommodated if the strip bends with the greater expanding metal on the outside of the curve where it can be longer.

A simple circuit using a bimetal strip is shown in Fig. 1.8. When the on/off switch of the appliance is closed a current will flow through the heating element, making use of the strip as part of the electrical circuit. Heat from the element will raise the temperature of the appliance and also that of the strip. The latter will begin to bend downwards and will eventually lose contact with point P. When this happens the current through the element will cease and so will heat production. Heat will now escape from the appliance by conduction, convection and

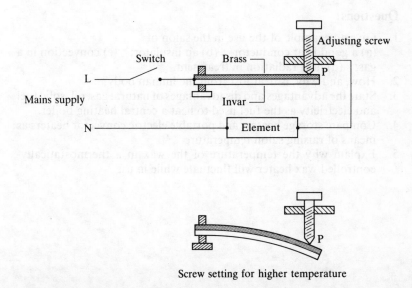

Screw setting for higher temperature

Fig. 1.8 The thermostat

radiation, and as a result the temperature will fall. This fall will cause the strip to straighten again and so it will re-make contact at P, allowing the current to flow again. The cycle of events will then be repeated. A graph showing temperature fluctuations is given in Fig. 1.9. By adjusting the pressure of the contact point P on the strip the average operating temperature of the appliance can be varied. For example, if the adjusting screw is turned so that it moves towards the strip, this will cause the latter to bend *before* any heat is generated. A higher temperature must then be reached in the appliance before the strip loses contact with P. This is also illustrated in Fig. 1.8.

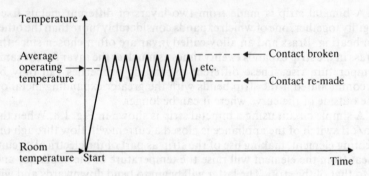

Fig. 1.9 Temperature of an appliance controlled by a thermostat

Questions

1. Give an example of the use in the salon of
   (a) a good heat conductor;   (b) an insulator;   (c) convection in a gas;   (d) heat radiation in treatment.
2. How, and why, is heat lost from the human body?
3. State the advantages and disadvantages of natural gas, oil, solid fuel and electricity as the fuel used to heat a central heating boiler.
4. Compare storage heaters and portable electric convector heaters as means of raising salon temperature.
5. Explain why the temperature of the wax in a thermostatically-controlled wax heater will fluctuate while in use.

Chapter 2

Ventilation of the salon

We have already seen that the beauty salon must be a place where the client relaxes and the therapist exercises the skills of her profession for the benefit of the client. Both of these purposes will be best served if the atmosphere of the salon to be breathed in approaches the composition of fresh air.

Composition of fresh air

Neglecting water vapour, the composition of the atmosphere ideal for human respiration will be

Nitrogen	78 per cent
Oxygen	21 per cent
Other gases	1 per cent

Oxygen, the gas essential for respiration, only accounts for about one-fifth of the atmosphere, but because the human body has evolved under such conditions, a greater proportion would upset normal metabolism. Pure oxygen may be administered during certain illnesses to speed up metabolism and assist recovery.

The 1 per cent of other gases is mostly made up of argon, a gas which has little or no chemical reaction with other substances but is used in gas-filled light bulbs. Suprisingly, the gas carbon dioxide, expired by ourselves and all living things during respiration and produced when fuels burn, only accounts for about 0.03 per cent of fresh air. Its level is kept low by the action of green plants containing chlorophyll which convert it to starch with the help of energy from sunlight. This process is known as *photosynthesis*.

Humidity and hygrometers

Fresh air normally contains, in addition to the gases listed above, a small percentage of water vapour. It is this that determines the *humidity* of the atmosphere. Although small, this percentage plays an important part in helping to decide whether the salon atmosphere will be comfortable for clients and staff.

At any given temperature there is an upper limit to the amount of water vapour the salon atmosphere can hold. If this were reached the air would be said to be *saturated* with water vapour. A rise in air temperature as for example in the sauna, would mean that more water vapour could be held before reaching saturation, but a fall in air temperature, as for example near windows, would have the reverse effect.

Disadvantages of *high humidity* include:

1. Condensation on colder walls and windows.
2. Difficulty in perspiring by clients and staff.
3. Inability of hair to retain a style owing to water absorption.

Disadvantages of *low humidity* include:

1. Loss of water from the skin resulting in a lack of softness.
2. Loss of water from fluids bathing the eyes, nostrils, mouth and throat resulting in soreness and an increased risk of infection.

In measuring and quoting values for the humidity of a salon it is usual to compare existing conditions with saturation. When we do this we are able to state the *relative humidity* (R.H.) of the salon atmosphere.

Examples:
1. If the atmosphere is half saturated its R.H. = 50 per cent.
2. R.H. = 75 per cent would mean the atmosphere is three-quarters saturated.

From the disadvantages of high and low humidity listed above it is easy to see that an ideal relative humidity for a salon would be 40 to 60 per cent but a wider range may be acceptable in practice.

Relative humidity is measured by using an instrument called a *hygrometer*. There are several types of hygrometer but those most likely to be encountered by the therapist are the following:

1. Hair hygrometer
This contains a small mesh of human hair fastened to the meter body at one end and to a tensioning spring at the other (see Fig. 2.1). As hair absorbs water from the atmosphere it is able to stretch more easily and this change causes a pointer to move around a scale, indicating a rise in humidity. A fall in humidity results in a loss of water from the hair causing the mesh to contract, so turning the pointer to lower values on the scale. The instrument is enclosed in a case which has holes around its sides to ensure that the air inside has the same humidity as that of the salon.

2. Wet and dry bulb hygrometer
This consists of two identical thermometers mounted side by side in the same case (see Fig. 2.2). One thermometer (the dry bulb) registers the

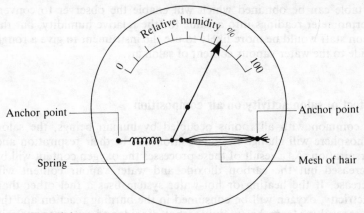

Fig. 2.1 The hair hygrometer

temperature of the salon. The other thermometer has its bulb surrounded by a piece of muslin tubing which reaches down into a small pot containing distilled water. This climbs up the spaces between the fibres of the muslin tube and evaporates into the air when it reaches the bulb. Cooling by evaporation takes place, causing the reading of the wet bulb thermometer to be lower than that of the dry bulb thermometer.

If the atmospheric humidity is low, evaporation will be easy and will produce a high cooling effect on the bulb. This means the difference between thermometer readings will be large. If the humidity is high the reverse situation will apply, so:

(a) a *large* difference in readings means *low* humidity;
(b) a *small* difference in readings means *high* humidity.

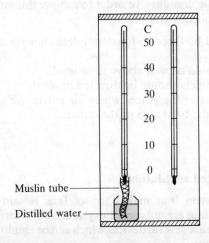

Fig. 2.2 Wet and dry-bulb hygrometer

A table can be obtained which will enable the observer to convert thermometer readings into a value for the relative humidity, but the salon staff would be more likely to use the instrument to give a rough guide to the water vapour content of salon air.

Effect of salon activity on air composition

In common with all rooms occupied by human beings, the salon atmosphere will change in composition due to their respiration and perspiration. As a result of these processes the oxygen content will be decreased but the carbon dioxide and water vapour content will increase. If the heating or hot-water system uses a fuel other than electricity, oxygen will be consumed in the burning reaction and the gases resulting from this (mainly carbon dioxide and water vapour) will either escape up a flue if fitted or into the salon atmosphere.

A number of salon facilities and treatments will influence the humidity in those parts of the salon where they are used including:

1. The shower cubicle, steam bath and facial steamer where humidity will be high due to the hot water.
2. The sauna, radiant heat and infra-red lamps where the temperature is higher and the air is able to hold more water vapour as a result. This means that the amount actually held is further away from saturation and so the relative humidity is effectively reduced.

Aims of a ventilation system

An ideal ventilation system for a salon would replace stale air by fresh air without causing draughts. In order to achieve this aim the following principles are applied where possible:

1. There should be three to four complete changes of the salon air every hour.
2. Air inlets should be well above floor level.
3. Air entering inlets should be directed upwards.
4. The total area of the places where air enters the salon should be greater than the total area of the outlets.

Natural and forced ventilation

A ventilation system that makes use of fans is said to use *forced* ventilation, but if fans are not used the system is considered to be *natural* ventilation. There are several devices which can be employed to improve natural ventilation:

1. Air bricks included in the structure of the building at a high level in the salon wall.
2. Hopper windows (see Fig. 2.3).
3. Louvre windows (see Fig. 2.4).
4. Cooper's disc fitted into a fixed window pane and capable of being rotated so that its holes coincide with matching holes in the window glass. Closed and partially-closed positions are also possible (see Fig. 2.5).

Natural ventilation receives considerable assistance if any form of convection heating is used, since this will tend to move air through the salon space from inlets to outlets. Disadvantages of natural ventilation include the possibility of draughts causing discomfort to clients and staff, and the problem of light articles being blown around. Dust, smells and insects may enter the salon and external sounds such as that of traffic may not be conducive to the ideal relaxed atmosphere. Incoming air may cause a lowering of salon temperature and so increase heating costs.

Air conditioning

If the salon is part of a much larger building such as a departmental store it may have its ventilation taken care of as part of an air-conditioning system. Since fans are used this will be an example of forced ventilation. Factors controlled by an air-conditioning system include:

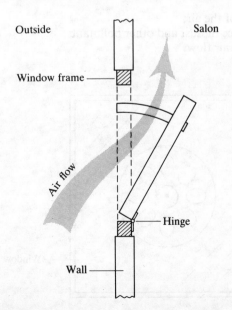

Fig. 2.3 Hopper window

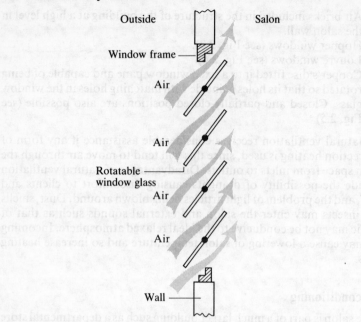

Fig. 2.4 Louvre window

(a) temperature;
(b) humidity;
(c) freshness of the air;
(d) the presence of dust and other pollutants;
(e) the rate of air flow.

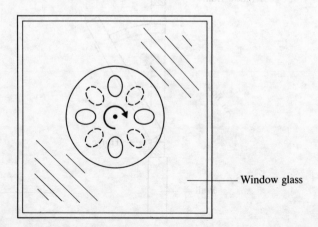

Fig. 2.5 Cooper's disc

Apart from fans, the system will also include a heater, humidifier, filters and some form of refrigeration unit which can reduce incoming air temperature in summer.

Questions

1. Consider a salon in which you have worked and discuss if the principles to be used in achieving a good ventilation system have been followed.
2. What is meant by the term *relative humidity*? Explain why its value may be (a) higher in the shower and (b) lower in the sauna, compared with the rest of the salon.
3. How does the composition of expired air compare with that of inspired air in a well-ventilated salon?
4. List the disadvantages of relying on the opening of casement windows only to improve the freshness of salon air.
5. Write short notes on: (a) photosynthesis; (b) hygrometers; (c) air conditioning.

Chapter 3

Salon water supply

In common with most places of employment, the beauty salon would not be able to function without a guaranteed supply of water that is free of germs, suspended matter and harmful dissolved substances. How this is achieved is the theme of this chapter.

Collection and treatment of water

All our water supplies originate from the oceans, lakes and other exposed water surfaces throughout the world. The energy of the sun in the form of heat radiation is used by water molecules in these surfaces to provide the latent heat required to evaporate into the atmosphere. Salts and other dissolved solids are left behind in the liquid water.

Convection currents now take this warm and moisture-laden air upwards to a level at which the temperature is sufficiently low for the humidity to reach saturation. Dust particles present in the atmosphere at these levels serve as nuclei around which water vapour can condense to form droplets. The clouds we see are large collections of these. Continued condensation on to them will increase their size and mass and eventually they will fall downwards in the form of rain. This process is called *precipitation*. If the clouds are formed at lower temperatures this precipitation will take the form of snow or hail. Water falling as rain will contain dissolved gases, the most soluble of which are carbon dioxide and sulphur dioxide. Both of these gases produce an acid when dissolved in water.

This rain water will now begin a downhill journey to the sea. For a time it may percolate through the ground of the hills but eventually it emerges as streams and rivers. These will flow into natural lakes and artificial reservoirs from which the salon supply will be obtained. Sometimes water is taken directly from larger rivers, even when these have already passed through towns at higher reaches. Waste water, already used by salons and other places of human activity, will find its way via the sewage works to rivers and finally to the sea. This whole process is known as the *water cycle* (see Fig. 3.1).

Reservoir and river water is not sufficiently pure for salon and other uses so it is passed through a water treatment works. A number of large storage tanks open to the atmosphere form the stages through which the

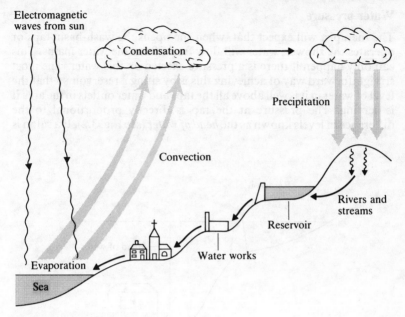

Fig. 3.1 The water cycle

water passes. The action of sunlight, atmospheric oxygen and the green algae that grow in these tanks serves to reduce the bacteria level in the water to a safe value. If this has not been achieved, treatment with chlorine forms the final stage.

To remove solid matter which may be either floating on the surface (leaves, for example) or suspended as fine particles within the water (clay, for example) several of the tanks are made in the form of filter beds. Stones and pebbles of graded size are laid inside the tank and the water filters through these. In some tanks the water will remain for a longer period of time so as to allow suspended matter to fall to the bottom as a sediment. This sediment is then left behind as the water moves on through the works.

Dissolved compounds are not normally removed, so regular checks must be made on their nature and concentration as the water enters the works. This will apply especially if the source is the lower reaches of a river. Water that is collected from hills made from calcium or magnesium compounds (e.g. limestone or gypsum) will contain dissolved salts due to the action of acids in rain on the hill rocks. They will result in the water being hard (see later this chapter). Granite or similar hard rock hills will be little affected by the passage of acid rain over them. Water collected here will be soft.

Water pressure

The therapist will expect that, when she opens the wash-basin taps or operates the shower, water will flow freely from the water mains. This can only happen if there is a pressure exerted on this water. The most straightforward way of achieving this is by siting a reservoir so that the level of water in it is well above all the taps and water outlets in the area it is serving. The pressure at the tap is directly proportional to the difference in levels known as the *head of water* (see Fig. 3.2). If a salon is

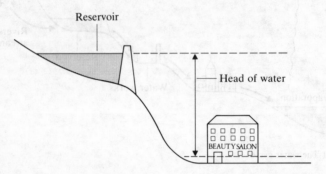

Fig. 3.2 Achieving water pressure

at a higher level than the water collecting point or if another range of hills separates them, it will be necessary to employ pumps to drive the mains water uphill. In such a situation a water tower may be sited on a suitable high point. The pumps will then keep this filled to a certain level, thus ensuring a steady pressure at the taps (see Fig. 3.3).

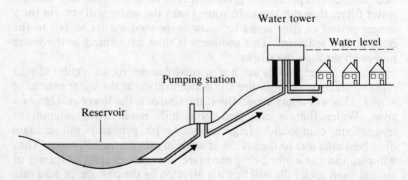

Fig. 3.3 The water tower

Distribution of cold and hot supplies to the salon

In Fig. 3.4 a simplified version of the likely layout of the pipes, etc. arranged to bring cold and hot water to the salon is shown. The pipe bringing water from the mains will be laid at some depth below ground level so as to be out of sight and, more importantly, to be insulated by the soil against low winter temperatures. An external *stop-tap* will be fitted to enable supplies to the building to be turned off in the event of leak or pipe burst. This stop-tap is often found at some depth below a metal cover in the outside ground surface and it may be necessary to have a special long-handled key to operate it. To make it more easy for the salon staff to turn off cold water supplies in an emergency, a second more accessible stop-tap is often fitted inside the building. Connections to all cold-water points are taken directly from this stop-tap.

Hot water may be produced by using a boiler-heated system as illustrated. In this, convection currents in the water cause hot water to rise to the hot-water storage tank while colder denser water falls to take its place in the boiler. Hot-water taps and shower may then be connected directly to the hot-water tank. To replenish water taken from the system a second storage tank is mounted at a greater height such as in the roof space. This has a pipe connection via a ball-valve to the mains cold water and an overflow pipe in case the valve fails to shut off. This system of water heating may be incorporated with a central-heating system.

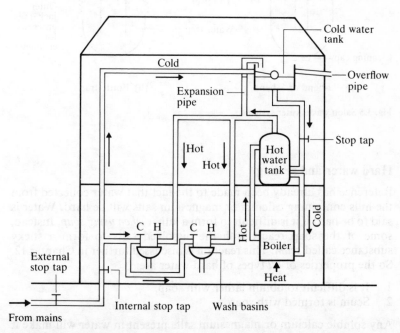

Fig. 3.4 Water supplies to the salon

Some salons may prefer not to have a boiler to produce hot water. In that case individual gas or electrically operated water heaters may be fitted at points where hot water is required. This is often the case for the shower. A connection to the cold-water supply will of course be necessary. Waste water from sinks and wash-basins will eventually find its way to the salon's drains and then the sewers. To prevent smells and bacteria finding their way into the salon from the sewers a *water-trap* is fitted below the drain-hole of the basin or sink. This is included in a *U-bend*, *S-bend* or *bottle trap* (see Fig. 3.5 (a) and (b)). Each of these has the advantage that solid objects such as jewellery accidentally lost in the waste pipe will be recoverable by emptying the trap.

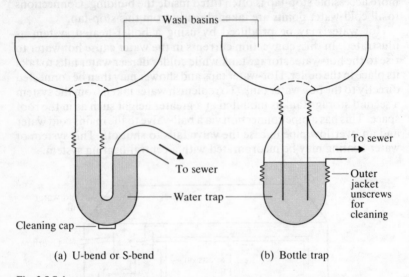

(a) U-bend or S-bend　　　　(b) Bottle trap

Fig. 3.5 Salon waste water systems

Hard water and scaling

Reference has already been made to the fact that water collected from the hills containing calcium or magnesium salts will be hard. Water is said to be hard if it is difficult to form a lather *when using soap*. Instead, some of the soap reacts with the dissolved salts to form a sticky substance called *scum*. This reaction is discussed further in Chapter 12. So the properties of *all* types of hard water are:

1. It is difficult to obtain lather with soap.
2. Scum is formed with soap.

Any soluble calcium or magnesium salts present in water will make it hard. Those most likely to be present in tap water are:

1. Calcium bicarbonate or magnesium bicarbonate.
2. Calcium chloride or magnesium chloride.
3. Calcium sulphate or magnesium sulphate.

A mixture of any of these will have the same effect.

Experiment 3.1 Comparison of water hardness

Fill a burette to above the zero mark with a standard soap solution using a small beaker. Place the beaker below the jet of the burette and run out solution until the liquid level is at zero. Pipette out a 25 cm³ sample of distilled water into a conical flask and then place this under the burette.

Now run out small quantities at a time of soap solution into the flask, shaking the contents after each addition. If lather bubbles are obtained which do not collapse immediately, start a stop-watch or clock and leave it running for two minutes. If lather persists after this time note the volume of soap solution that has been added.

Repeat the test with 25 cm³ samples of salon tap water, tap water from other areas, rain-water, etc. and compare their hardnesses. If only soft tap-water is available try the effect of adding to a sample a small flake of fused calcium chloride.

In the case of hardness due to *bicarbonates* there is an additional problem which is likely to be of far greater consequence to a salon than the lack of lather and scum problem. This is the production of *scale* which occurs wherever the water is heated and due to the reaction:

Calcium or magnesium bicarbonate ──heat──► calcium or magnesium carbonate + carbon dioxide + water

This insoluble calcium or magnesium carbonate scale deposited in pipes will reduce their effective diameter and hence the rate of water flow. Scale deposited around the element of an electric water-heater acts as an insulator, causing the element temperature to rise and finally burn out. A salon that uses a boiler for hot water or central heating will have a similar problem.

Prolonged boiling can soften water containing bicarbonates, making use of the reaction given above, but it has no effect on chloride or sulphate hardness, so we sometimes distinguish between:

(a) temporary hardness due to bicarbonates, and
(b) permanent hardness due to chlorides and sulphates.

A salon situated in a hard-water area may find it necessary to soften the water prior to use. In common with all salts, those of calcium and magnesium which can be the cause of hardness exist in the form of particles known as *ions* when dissolved in water. Each salt produces two types of ion, one carrying a positive charge and the other a negative charge. For example, calcium sulphate exists as positive calcium ions and negative sulphate ions. The ion common to all three calcium salts is the calcium ion, while the ion common to the magnesium salts is the magnesium ion, and these are the particles responsible for the water hardness. A number of sodium salts added to the water can remove the calcium and magnesium ions present. These include:

1. Sodium carbonate (washing soda).
2. Sodium borate (borax).
3. Sodium hexametaphosphate.

The hexametaphosphate is probably the best as it does not form an insoluble precipitate.

  None of the water softeners above can be conveniently used to prevent scaling. To do this it will be necessary to soften the water before it reaches any form of heating. This can be done by incorporating in the salon's plumbing system a cylinder containing an insoluble substance through which the water percolates and which is able to remove calcium and magnesium ions replacing them with sodium ions. This process is known as *ion exchange* (see Fig. 3.6). Natural or synthetic *sodium aluminium silicate* and certain synthetic resins are able to perform this function. The reaction taking place during ion-exchange can be represented thus:

calcium ions + sodium aluminium silicate ⟶ sodium ions + calcium aluminium silicate

These ion-exchange materials cannot be expected to soften water for an indefinite period of time. Eventually all sodium ions in them will have

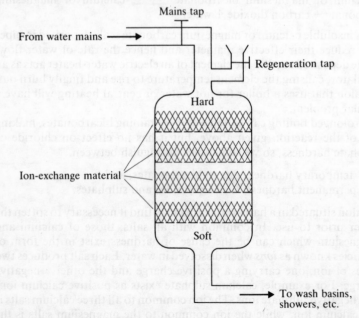

Fig. 3.6 Ion-exchange water softening

been replaced by calcium and magnesium ions, so they must now be *regenerated*. This is done by passing a concentrated common salt solution through the cylinder instead of the mains water. The sodium ions from the salt enter the softening substance, flush out the calcium and magnesium ions and so the ion-exchange material is ready to function again.

All of the water softeners referred to above are able to soften both temporary and permanent hardness.

Questions

1. Explain why the water supply to the salon where you are training or have worked is either hard or soft by referring to the area of the country where it is collected.
2. What action would you take if a serious leak occurred (a) in the salon cold-water system, and (b) in the salon hot-water system?
3. What is the function of: (a) a water tower; (b) a bottle trap; (c) an ion-exchange resin?
4. Describe and explain the action on calcium bicarbonate of (a) heat and (b) sodium carbonate.

Chapter 4

Electricity in the salon

In common with the community as a whole, the modern beauty salon will make considerable use of electrical appliances. Not only will these be for the production of heat and light, and for the general good housekeeping of the salon, but many of the treatments offered to clients will involve the use of electricity. It is important therefore that the therapist at an early stage in her training becomes aware of the nature of electricity and how to make safe use of it. Basic principles are covered in this chapter with a more detailed look at electrical machines in Chapters 16 and 17.

Static electricity

Historically this was the first form of electricity discovered, but it still can cause problems in the salon of today. Static electricity is generated when two surfaces rub together, hence its alternative name of *frictional electricity*. It is normally only noticed if these surfaces are of two non-metallic substances. Material like wool which absorbs water from the air also needs to be dry, and humidity needs to be low.

The presence of a static charge can be shown by:

1. Attraction between objects especially if one is of light weight (see Exp. 4.1).
2. Small crackles of sound.
3. Tiny flashes of light, especially when the general illumination is at a low level.
4. Electric shocks.

Experiment 4.1   Attractive force due to static charges
Tear up a small piece of preferably thin paper into approximately squares of one centimetre side and place on a horizontal surface. Comb the hair with a non-metallic comb and then place the latter just above the paper pieces. The force of attraction should make these jump up to the comb. Repeat the experiment rubbing a plastic pen body on an overall sleeve instead of combing the hair.

To explain the generation of a static charge we need to make use of the fact that the atoms in all materials contain two types of electrically charged particles. These are *protons* (positive charge) and *electrons* (negative charge). The charge carried by an electron is as large as that carried by a proton but, being of opposite signs, they can cancel each other out. All types of atoms have equal numbers of protons and electrons so to the outside world they appear to be electrically neutral. Compared with protons, electrons are of very light weight (low mass) and some are found in the outer regions of the atom well away from the protons. Examples of the way electrons are arranged around the nucleus of an atom are shown in Fig. 4.1.

When two surfaces rub together, the atoms from which they are made are moved close to each other and this has the effect of dislodging the outer electrons from one surface and transferring them to the other. When the surfaces are subsequently separated one has gained electrons and the other has lost electrons. Thus:

(a) the surface that gained electrons has more electrons than protons and so becomes *negatively-charged*;
(b) the surface that lost electrons has more protons than electrons and so becomes *positively-charged* (see Fig. 4.2).

The same forces of attraction existing between the protons in a nucleus and the surrounding electrons also manifests itself whenever a positive electric charge is situated near to a negative electric charge, so two statically-charged surfaces produced by rubbing together will then attract each other. This is why the hair is shown attracted to the comb in Fig. 4.2 (a) and (b). Conversely, when like charges are close to each other, a force of repulsion exists trying to drive them apart. Positive charges repel each other; negative charges repel each other. This is why statically-charged hairs on the head will not lie down beside each other. We shall see this repulsion effect put to use in the action of some emulsifiers and detergents in Chapter 12.

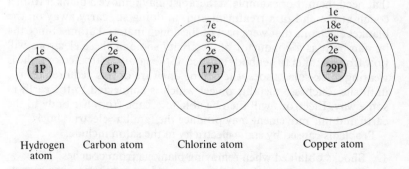

Hydrogen atom   Carbon atom   Chlorine atom   Copper atom

P = proton (in central nucleus)
e = electron (in surrounding shells)

Fig. 4.1 Structure of atoms

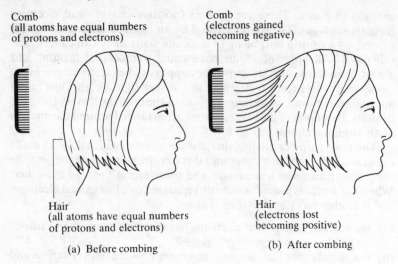

Comb
(all atoms have equal numbers
of protons and electrons)

Comb
(electrons gained
becoming negative)

Hair
(all atoms have equal numbers
of protons and electrons)

Hair
(electrons lost
becoming positive)

(a) Before combing

(b) After combing

Fig. 4.2 Explanation of static charge generation

The small crackles of sound and the tiny flashes of light occur when oppositely-charged surfaces come into contact. Electrons jump back again to join the atoms that need them and in doing so set free the energy that was required to separate them from their parent atoms during the rubbing process. This energy is radiated as sound and light. This is often noticed when a garment is removed after being worn for some time and then allowed to fall together in a bundle as, for example, when taking off a sweater, blouse or shirt.

Static electric shocks usually involve the escape of a static charge to the earth. Our planet is such a large object that it has a very large surface area. There is plenty of room to store electrons received from other objects, and there are plenty of electrons available to supply to objects that need them. For example, a therapist may remove a blanket from a couch at the end of a treatment and, in doing so, carry away on the blanket electrons that were part of the couch material atoms. Since the human body is a conductor of electricity some of these electrons will flow from blanket to her body surface. If the salon is carpeted or if she is wearing thick-soled shoes, she will be unaware of this acquired charge until she touches a metallic object which is connected to the earth in some way. Electrons will then be able to escape from her body to the earth and this movement may produce the familiar electric shock.

Problems caused by static electricity in the salon include:

1. Shocks obtained when removing blankets from couches.
2. Shocks obtained after walking around on synthetic fibre carpets and then touching a metallic object such as the till.
3. The figure-hugging effect of a nylon overall that has not been pre-treated to prevent static build-up.

4. The attraction of dirt particles to inside hem-lines.
5. The difficulty of styling fine hair with non-metallic brushes and combs.

Circuits

The flow of electrons in a metallic object as described in the previous section is referred to as an *electric current*. Currents can also flow in solutions in water of electrolytes (acids, alkalis and salts). The particles that move then are known as *ions*. If dissolved in water an electrolyte produces both positively-charged ions called *cations* and negatively-charged ions called *anions*. (As an aid to memory, note that n is for negative and there are two such letters in the word anion.) An electric current can thus take two forms:

(a) a flow of electrons if in a metal;
(b) a flow of ions if in an electrolyte solution.

Electric currents can be used to produce a number of different effects such as heating and movement but need to flow for a controllable length of time to be of benefit in the salon. Two essential ingredients must be present for this to be achieved and these are:

1. A device capable of pumping electrons and ions around, usually a *battery* or *generator*.
2. A complete path of conducting materials joining the terminals of the battery or generator and known as the *circuit*.

After silver, *copper* is the best conductor of electricity and is used extensively in all the various types of circuit used in the salon. These range from the thick cables and flex that carry mains currents to the delicate connecting wires used inside a faradic machine for linking up the components needed to generate its complex currents. Other metals such as *tungsten* and the alloy *nichrome* are used as part of a circuit for their special properties, as will be seen later in this chapter and in Chapter 5. In salon treatments which involve connecting pairs of pads to a client, a current flows through the client's tissues and these conduct electricity because living cells and the fluid which bathes them contain electrolytes dissolved in water.

When there are two or more components in a circuit they can be connected in different ways, giving what are called *series circuits* and *parallel circuits* (see Fig. 4.3 (a) and (b)). Parallel circuits are the most common because they have the advantage that the current flowing in one parallel path is often little affected by changes occurring in the other. For example, in Fig. 4.3 if the filament of lamp B breaks, lamp A will also go out in the series circuit but will remain lit in the parallel

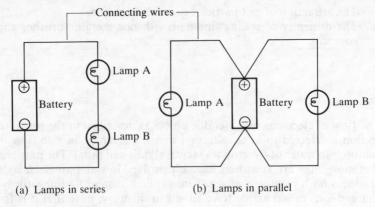

(a) Lamps in series   (b) Lamps in parallel

Fig. 4.3 Series and parallel circuits

circuit. Electrical appliances used in the salon which are also mains-operated are always connected in parallel.

Electrical units

A battery or generator is able to drive a current around a circuit by exerting electrical pressure. *Electrical pressure* is measured in *volts* . The number of electrons or ions that pass a given point in the circuit every second is directly related to the current intensity. *Current intensity* is measured in *amps*. An ammeter is an instrument for registering current intensity.

Experiment 4.2 Factors affecting current intensity
Connect a twelve-volt lamp, such as those used in light experiments, in series with an ammeter whose scale reads up to five amps. Complete the circuit by connecting to a variable-voltage power pack as shown in Fig. 4.4. Select the two-volt position of the pack by either setting the control switch or plugging into the appropriate sockets. Switch on the pack and note the reading of the meter. Repeat the measurements every two-volt increment up to a maximum of twelve volts. Note how increases in electrical pressure produce increases in current intensity and that the lamp filament may not glow if the current intensity is too low.

With the power-pack voltage kept constant at one of the values already used, replace the lamp by other suitable circuit components such as resistance wire coils and note how the current intensities obtained compare with that passing through the lamp at the same electrical pressure.

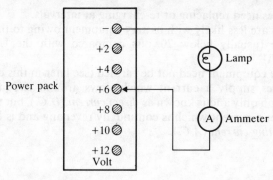

Fig. 4.4 Current intensity factors

A circuit which only allows low current intensities for a given electrical pressure is said to possess a *high electrical resistance*, whereas a circuit which allows high current intensities is said to possess a *low electrical resistance*. Electrical resistance is measured in *ohms*. Its value for a given circuit will depend on the materials used to make its component parts and also on the thickness and length of any wire included.

From Experiment 4.2 it can be seen that two factors control the current intensity in a circuit. These are the electrical pressure exerted by the battery, generator or power pack and the resistance of the circuit. They can be combined in a formula from which current intensities can be calculated:

Current intensity = $\dfrac{\text{Electrical pressure}}{\text{Electrical resistance}}$ or Amps = $\dfrac{\text{Volts}}{\text{Ohms}}$

Example: If the resistance of the body tissues between the pads fastened to a client receiving faradic treatment is 5,000 ohm, what current intensity will flow if the machine electrical pressure is 25 volts?

Amps = $\dfrac{25}{5,000}$ = 5/1,000 or five milliamp

Mains-operated and battery-operated equipment

A comparison between using the electrical mains or using batteries for supplying the electrical pressure to different circuits and appliances in the salon leads to the following conclusions:

1. Battery equipment is more portable.

2.   Batteries need replacing or re-charging at intervals.
3.   Shocks are less likely with battery equipment owing to their lower voltage (usually below 20 volts compared with the UK mains 240 volt).
4.   Battery equipment need not be earthed (see later in this chapter).
5.   Batteries supply a current which flows around circuits in one direction only and is known as *direct current* (*D.C.*), but the mains supplies a current which is continually reversing and is known as *alternating current* (*A.C.*).

Fuses

A fuse is usually a piece of thin copper wire included in a circuit, which melts, or fuses, if the current intensity exceeds a certain value. This value will depend on the thickness of the fuse wire.

Experiment 4.3   Demonstration of fuse action
Connect up the circuit shown in Fig. 4.5 and slide the variable resistor so that all its wire is in the circuit. Calculate, using its resistance value, the approximate voltage required to obtain a current intensity of about 2 amps and set the power pack accordingly. Switch on and slowly reduce the amount of resistance wire in the circuit until the fuse wire melts. Notice how this break in the circuit has stopped the current flowing.

The purpose of a fuse is to prevent an appliance or a circuit in a building from taking an excessive current intensity which could result in overheating, damage and possible fire. There are two types of fuse which should concern a beauty therapist. These are:

1.   Cartridge fuses found in plugs at the end of the flex leads and used to

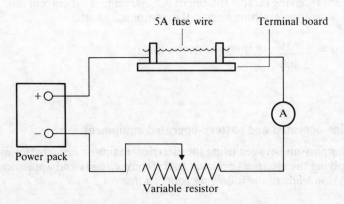

Fig. 4.5 Demonstration of fuse action

protect the appliance to which the flex is connected. Their structure is shown in Fig. 4.6.

2. Wire fuses found in fuse boxes near to the salon meter and used to protect the salon circuits. After switching off the main switch, the wire carrier made of a ceramic material can be removed and a new piece of fuse wire threaded through to connect to end screws. The value of the fuse wire required is usually stated on the carrier. Sometimes *miniature circuit breakers* are used instead of wire fuses. They have the advantage of being easy to re-set once the cause of the excessive current is discovered and put right. Cartridge fuses are also sometimes used for this purpose.

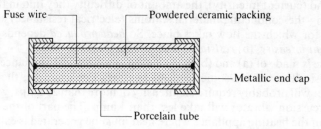

Fuse wire — — Powdered ceramic packing

— Metallic end cap

— Porcelain tube

Fig. 4.6 The cartridge fuse

If a new piece of salon electrical equipment is purchased, it is important to make sure that the correct value of fuse is fitted in the plug. To decide what this must be it is necessary to know what is the current intensity taken by the appliance when functioning correctly. Some manufacturers state this on a label fitted to the appliance, but it is more usual to find on the label a voltage value and also the wattage. This latter refers to the power of the appliance, that is the amount of energy consumed from the mains every second. *Electrical power* is measured in *watts*. The normal current intensity for an appliance can be calculated by using the formula:

$$\text{Amps} = \frac{\text{Watts}}{\text{Volts}}$$

Example: What is the current intensity taken by a 1,000 watt wax heater when operated on the 240 volt mains supply?

$$\text{Amps} = \frac{1,000}{240} = 4.17$$

Cartridge fuses can be obtained in a number of different ratings including 1 amp, 2 amp, 3 amp, 5 amp and 13 amp. In the example above, if a 3 amp fuse is fitted it will melt the first time the heater is switched on because 4.17 amp will flow. The best fuse to fit will be of a

5 amp rating as the current intensity only has to increase a little and then the fuse will automatically switch off. A 13 amp fuse would allow three times the normal current intensity before operating. The appliance would certainly be damaged by then. So to fit the correct fuse, note or calculate the normal number of amps taken and then choose the *next highest rating* available.

Heating effect of an electric current

When electrons or ions flow through a conductor the amount of energy converted to heat depends on the number of particles flowing every second (current intensity), the amount of difficulty they find in flowing among the conducting material's atoms (electrical resistance) and the time for which the flow takes place. So *heat produced* depends on (a) *current intensity*, (b) *resistance* and (c) *time*.

Use is made of (a) and (b) in designing any electrical appliance which is basically used for some form of heating. For example, the sauna heater will probably require an intensity of more than 20 amps, whereas a percussion vibrator will take less than 1 amp. The part of the circuit within the heating appliance where heat must be generated is called the *heating element*. This will be made of wire which is a poorer conductor than copper and is known as *resistance wire*. The alloy *nichrome* is often used for this purpose as it is not susceptible to the chemical attack of atmospheric oxygen even when hot. Thin wire possesses more resistance than thick wire of the same material and length so it may be used where heat is required. The use of thin *tungsten* wire as the filament in ordinary light bulbs is an example of this. To avoid getting heat in the wrong place when using high current intensities, cables and flex are made of low resistance copper and thick cables will be used to supply power points, showers, saunas, etc.

Mains flex and its connections

The international colour code for the insulating material surrounding the three cores of the mains flex is as follows:

1. Live is brown (used to be red).
2. Neutral is blue (used to be black).
3. Earth is yellow/green (used to be green).

The earth wire, if fitted, is a safety device designed to prevent the person using the appliance from receiving a possible shock. It will only be present if the appliance has metal parts which can be touched when it is switched on. It will be connected to these parts so that, should the live wire inside the appliance lose its insulating sleeve or become disconnected and make contact with the metal parts also, there is no risk of shock. The earth wire will prove to be a much better path for a current to run to the earth than the body of the person using the appliance. The risk of the live wire becoming exposed in this way can be considerably reduced if it is *double-insulated*. Where this is done, use of an earth wire is not necessary. Appliances which are double-insulated are marked with the symbol ▢

In Fig. 4.7(a),(b),(c) the connections of the flex to a wax heater and its plug are shown, and also the connections from the power socket. Important points to note are:

1. The cartridge fuse and switch are always in the live lead.
2. The earth wire is connected to the metal case inside the appliance.
3. The earth socket is connected to ground.
4. Live and neutral are connected to opposite ends of the heating element and may be interchanged if required.

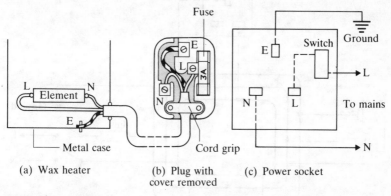

(a) Wax heater   (b) Plug with cover removed   (c) Power socket

Fig. 4.7 Flex connections

Ring main for power sockets

Figure 4.8 shows how the sockets of a modern salon will be connected by cables to the place where the mains supply enters. This arrangement is known as a *ring main*. It has a number of advantages over older methods of connection including:

(a) the total length of cable used will be less;
(b) since current will flow both ways round the ring to reach the socket chosen, thinner cables may be employed;
(c) any appliance can be plugged into any socket;
(d) each appliance will have its own protecting fuse in the plug;
(e) it is easier and cheaper to add more sockets to the ring.

Prior to the introduction of the ring main, individual power sockets were often connected by three cables directly to the fuse box and this could involve quite long lengths if the socket was situated at a remote part of the building. Two types of socket were used, one intended for appliances taking up to 5 amps and the other for appliances taking up to 15 amps. This meant the appliance had to be fitted with a plug which fitted the appropriate socket and so could not be plugged into the other type, even though the latter might be sited more conveniently. The plugs used did not contain a fuse, so if a fault developed in the appliance it led to a fuse blowing in the fuse box.

Paying for electricity

The electricity bill for the salon will show on it the number of *units* used both at the standard rate and at off-peak rate, if applicable. This number

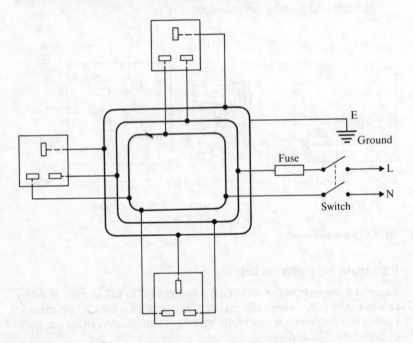

Fig. 4.8 The ring main

will have been obtained from readings by the meter inspector during visits. Most electricity meters now have digital read-outs and make it easy for the salon owner to keep a check on salon consumption. The bill will also state the price per unit and any standing charges made. A *unit* of electricity is consumed by a *1 kilowatt* (1,000 watt) appliance left switched on for *one hour*. This assumes that the appliance is not switched on and off by a thermostat during this time. The unit is also known as a *kilowatt-hour* for this reason. To calculate the cost of using any electrical appliance we use the formula:

$$\text{Units} = \frac{\text{Watts}}{1,000} \times \text{hours}$$

and then apply the price per unit as shown on the electricity bill.
Example: How much will it cost to operate an 8,000 watt electrically heated shower for a total of two hours during a salon working day if electricity is 5p per unit?

$$\text{Units} = \frac{8,000}{1,000} \times 2 = 16 \qquad 16 \text{ units at 5p each} = 80p$$

Questions

1. Drawing on the experience of yourself and your colleagues, describe how static electricity can cause problems in the beauty salon.
2. Where would you expect to find the following substances being used in connection with electricity in the salon:
   (a) brass, (b) tungsten, (c) polyvinyl chloride, or PVC, (d) porcelain?
3. Explain why:
   (a) heating elements are made from nichrome wire;
   (b) copper fuse wire is thinner than the bundle of wires in flex;
   (c) appliances with all-plastic cases need not be earthed.
4. A portable convector heater is rated at 2 kilowatts and is designed to operate on the 240 volt mains. Calculate:
   (a) the fuse required in the plug if 3-amp, 5-amp and 13-amp cartridge fuses are available;
   (b) the cost of using it for six hours if electricity is 5p per unit.
5. Which unit is used to measure:
   (a) the power of an electrical appliance?
   (b) the current intensity passing through a circuit?
   (c) the resistance of a lamp filament?
   (d) the electrical pressure exerted by a battery?

Chapter 5

Light, colour, and salon illumination

It is quite a commonplace to hear someone say that beauty is in the eye of the beholder and it is an expression that would be supported by modern scientific knowledge. Without light entering our eyes from the people and objects around us we should be unable to appreciate fully their shape, colour and texture. A beauty salon, therefore, is a place where correct illumination is important and a beauty therapist is a person who must understand the behaviour of light as it reveals the world around us.

Reflection and mirrors

Light spreads outwards in the form of waves from the sources where it is generated whether this be from the sun, ordinary filament lamps, fluorescent lamps or other type of lamp. The direction in which these waves are travelling at any point in space is called a *ray*, and use is made of these rays to explain the behaviour of light under various circumstances. Rays form straight lines while light is travelling in the same substance, or *medium*, but changes occur when the boundary between two media is reached. At such a boundary some light may be:

1. Reflected back into the original medium.
2. Absorbed into the new medium as another form of energy.
3. Allowed to travel in the new medium, perhaps after changing direction.

The proportions of the incident light falling on the boundary that are treated in these three ways will depend on the optical properties of the two media.

Figure 5.1 illustrates the laws that control the manner in which light is reflected. These laws are:

1. Incident ray, reflected ray and normal line lie in the same plane.
2. Angle of incidence (A) = angle of reflection (B).

Each ray reflected from a surface will behave in this way.

The most common type of mirror with a very flat smooth surface is known as a *plane mirror* and in it we see an image of ourselves and our surroundings. An image of any object seen in this mirror is the same size

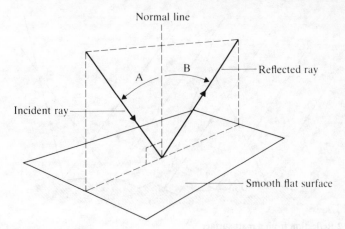

Fig. 5.1 Reflection of light

as the object itself and appears to be as far behind the mirror as the object is in front. When the mirror surface is *convex*, smaller images are seen but more of the surroundings is included in the field of view. This is why convex mirrors are used for security purposes and could as such find a use in the salon. To obtain an enlarged image for use in self make-up a *concave* mirror will be suitable but it must not be too curved or smaller and inverted images will be seen.

All smooth surfaces will tend to show images in them like mirrors, but these may not be sharp, and if the surface is very curved, lines of brightness will appear along curved corners. These effects are the cause of *shine*. Smooth surfaces are shiny surfaces. It is fashionable for hair to look shiny which means that each hair shaft surface must be smooth. Many hair treatments such as perming and bleaching tend to leave a rough surface and so are followed in the hairdressing salon by the application of a conditioner to restore the smoothness. In a similar way, nail varnish should dry to leave a smooth and, therefore, glossy appearance. Whether this is achieved will be partly determined by its composition (see Ch. 8).

In facial make-up shine must be avoided and this is achieved by applying powder at the end of the treatment. The tiny particles of the powder settle on the face to give a matt finish which is sufficiently rough for the light falling on it to be scattered in all directions as shown in Fig. 5.2. Each ray of light falling on the surface obeys the laws of reflection but the irregularities of the surface cause the scatter. Light is known to be a form of wave motion moving outwards from its source and the distance between corresponding points on successive waves is called its *wavelength*. This will be given further consideration in Chapter 19. Because the wavelength of light is so small, only a mildly-rough surface is necessary to lose shine. Rough surfaces are matt surfaces.

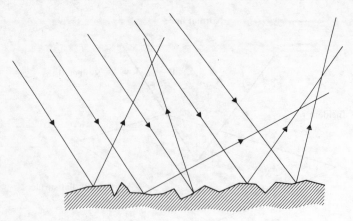

Fig. 5.2 Reflection from a matt surface

Experiment 5.1   Reflection from smooth and rough surfaces
Fasten a piece of white paper to a drawing board and then mount a plane
mirror so that it stands at right-angles to the paper surface. Connect up a
ray box so that it produces a wide beam of light and allow this to fall at
an angle of about forty-five degrees to the mirror. Notice how the beam
is reflected. Replace the mirror by a piece of white card and observe the
difference in the illumination of the paper. It may be necessary here to
tilt the card forward to see the effect.

Refraction and lenses

When light enters a new transparent medium, the velocity at which it
travels may be changed. In general, if it crosses from air into a denser
medium such as water, glass or an acrylic plastic, it will have its velocity
reduced. The reverse will apply if the light leaves a dense medium and
enters air. This change in velocity will only produce a visible effect if the
light rays hit the boundary between the media at an angle to the normal
line. Figure 5.3 shows how the direction of travel of the light changes
under these circumstances and the effect is known as *refraction*.
Refraction occurs at P and Q in the figure. The laws controlling the angle
changes in refraction are more complex than those controlling reflection
and will not be dealt with here.

The most important application of refraction for the beauty therapist
is the *lens*. A lens is made of a transparent substance in which light
travels more slowly than in air. When light enters and leaves the lens it
will be refracted, but, because of the curved surfaces used, a number of
effects can be produced. A lens having two *convex* surfaces is used in the
salon where *magnification* is required. It may be used during epilation or

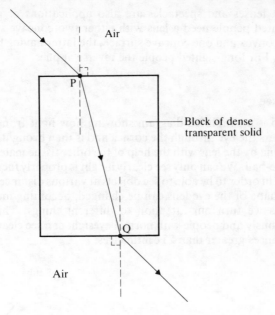

Fig. 5.3 Refraction of light

in examining the skin and is often mounted with a small circular fluorescent lamp on an adjustable arm. If the object being observed through the lens is close to it, the eye will see an enlarged image of that object apparently behind the lens. A convex lens receiving light from an object much further away will cause focusing of the rays at some point (see Fig. 5.4). This is the action of the lens in the human eye which brings light to a focus on the retina and so creates an image.

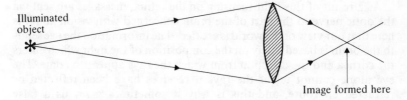

Fig. 5.4 Focusing action of a convex lens

Care must be taken in the salon in positioning the magnifying lenses when not in use. If direct sunlight is allowed to pass through them it will be brought to a focus producing a concentration of energy at some point. If this happens to be on the surface of a piece of flammable material such as paper, plastic or thin textile, a fire could result.

Contact lenses and spectacles are also applications of refraction. Short-sighted people need a lens with either two concave surfaces or with one convex and one concave surface, the latter having the greater curvature. For long-sighted people the reverse applies.

How we see

Figure 5.5 is a simplified diagram showing how light from a distant object enters the eye through the cornea and is then brought to a focus on the retina by the lens with the help of the other tissue material which fills the eye-ball. We can only see clearly if light is properly focused at the retina, so, in order to be able to see objects at various distances from the eye, the shape of the eye lens can be changed, becoming more or less convex, as we turn our attention to different things. This is done subconsciously and people with normal eyesight can see clearly objects at all distances greater than 25 centimetres.

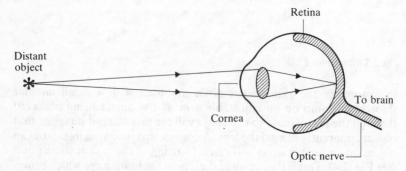

Retina

Distant object

To brain

Cornea

Optic nerve

Fig. 5.5 The human eye and vision

As a result of this light-focusing on the retina, messages are sent via the optic nerve to the part of the brain concerned with vision and it is here that our view of the world is created. The information the eye sends to the brain is based solely on the composition of the light which enters the cornea and the direction from which the rays appear to come. The eye alone cannot tell if the rays it receives have been reflected or refracted en route, and this is why it sometimes gives us a false impression of the world outside. Examples of this are when we see our own image apparently *behind* the make-up mirror or the unusually *large* facial hairs of a client through the magnifying lens.

Why objects are coloured

It was Isaac Newton who first demonstrated that white light is really a mixture of different coloured lights. He did this by allowing a shaft of sunlight to pass through a piece of glass in the geometrical shape called a *prism* (see Fig. 5.6). Newton said he could see seven colours emerging from the prism in the form of a *spectrum*. These he called red, orange, yellow, green, blue, indigo and violet. It is now known that the difference in the light waves that produce these colours is one of wavelength (see Ch. 19), and that the shorter the wavelength the more the light is refracted by the glass. Because of the shape of the prism, the refraction that occurs when the light enters is not cancelled out by the refraction on leaving and so the colours are separated, or dispersed. Separation of white light into colours occurs under other conditions too. The therapist will be familiar with the colours seen when oil-spills float on water, and she may have noticed colours in the surface of acrylic plastic containers when looked at in reflected light.

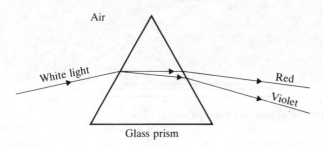

Fig. 5.6 Dispersion of white light by a prism

Salons are normally illuminated by some form of white light and it is this that falls on the people and objects present. If an object is both transparent and coloured, such as a ruby or an emerald, the effect illustrated in Fig. 5.7 takes place. It acts as a colour filter, only allowing one of the seven colours present in the white light to pass through. The

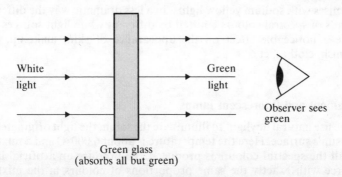

Fig. 5.7 Action of light on a coloured transparent object

coloured object must contain one or more chemical compounds capable of using up the energy of all the colours which do not get through.

A similar explanation can be given for the colour of an opaque object except that in this case the coloured light that cannot be absorbed is reflected and this is what the observer sees (see Fig. 5.8). In white light, extremes of this explanation of the cause of colour would be:

1. An object that *absorbs all* colours will look *black*.
2. An object that *reflects all* colours will look *white*.

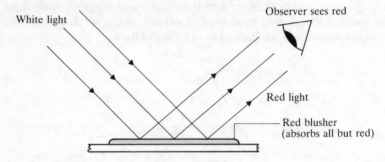

Fig. 5.8 Action of light on a coloured opaque object

Effect of incident light on colour rendering

It was assumed in the previous section that the light falling on an object would be white. Suppose in each example illustrated sodium yellow light were used instead. This light is confined to one narrow wavelength band only. There is only yellow light present and this would be absorbed by any green or red object. In each case no light would enter the observer's eyes so each would look black. The apparently soiled appearance of the skin in such yellow street lights can be explained in this way.

Although a salon owner would never choose to illuminate the premises with sodium yellow lights, in a less dramatic way the different blends of spectral colours emitted by different white light sources can have a noticeable effect on the appearance of skin, make-up, nail varnish, clothes, etc.

Filament and fluorescent lamps

If we use natural daylight to illuminate the salon, the light originates on the sun's surface. Here the temperature is about 6,000°C and a mixture of all the spectral colours is produced. To produce an artificial light source with exactly the same proportions of colours in the mixture would involve taking a substance up to 6,000°C also. All known substances will have vaporised on reaching this temperature. In a *filament lamp* a thin piece of tungsten wire wound in the form of an open spiral is mounted inside a glass bulb. It is connected to much thicker wires which pass through the glass of the bulb to the lamp cap (see Fig. 5.9). A current is passed through the filament which causes its temperature to rise, but, since the melting point of tungsten is 3,380°C, the current intensity must be limited so that the wire does not melt. In practice, temperatures well below this are reached. The bulb will have all the air removed from it during manufacture and may then be either left empty (vacuum lamp) or filled with argon gas (gas-filled lamp). This is to prevent oxygen from the air converting tungsten wire to powdery tungsten oxide on first heating up.

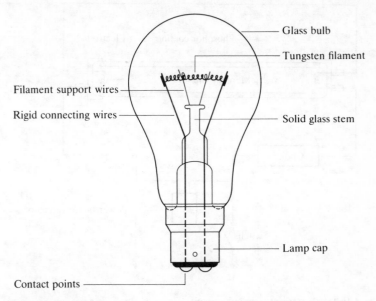

Fig. 5.9 The filament lamp

Filament lamps are very inefficient light sources, only converting about 10 per cent of the electrical energy they use to light. The rest appears as heat. A more efficient way of producing light is to pass a current through a gas or vapour using electrodes to lead it in and out. Unfortunately, gases and vapours excited by the passage of a current through them tend to produce light containing only some parts of the spectrum. We have already seen this happening in sodium vapour. When a current passes through mercury vapour, however, some of the waves produced are in the invisible ultra-violet band (see Ch. 19).

This is made use of in the *fluorescent lamp* which consists of a glass tube with electrodes fitted at each end and connected to leads which pass out of the tube to the end caps (see Fig. 5.10). The tube has the air pumped out of it during manufacture and a small shot of liquid mercury is added just before sealing up. The mercury vaporises in the empty space inside the tube. On the inside of the tube is deposited a thin layer of a substance known as a *phosphor* which has the ability to trap ultra-violet waves and convert their energy into visible light waves which then emerge from the tube. The phosphor is said to *fluoresce*. By choosing different phosphors the proportions of the spectral colours in the light emitted can be varied.

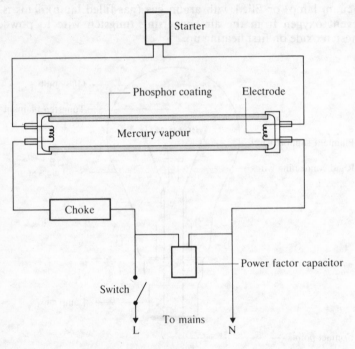

Fig. 5.10 The fluorescent lamp in its circuit

A fluorescent lamp cannot be connected to the mains in as simple a way as a filament lamp. It must have a circuit component connected in series with it which limits the current intensity. A device known as a *choke* is usually employed which will probably cost more than the lamp itself but will have a very long life. In addition, the lamp will not start to conduct electricity unless a high voltage is applied across the electrodes. The mains voltage is not high enough for this, so a *starter* must also be included in the circuit which, in conjunction with the choke, gives an initial high voltage surge. The lamp will then continue to conduct at mains voltage.

A comparison between filament and fluorescent lamps shows:

(a) fluorescent lamps are more expensive to install;
(b) fluorescent lamps last several times longer;
(c) fluorescent lamps give much more light for the same amount of electrical energy;
(d) fluorescent lamps can be purchased giving different types of white light;
(e) filament lamps are more versatile in their uses owing to their shape, although miniature compact fluorescent lamps are now made which can be used in filament lamp sockets.

Salon illumination

When designing a salon an important consideration must be the choice of lighting to illuminate the different areas of the salon and the activities that will take place there. There are three types of light source available:

1. Natural daylight via windows and sky-lights.
2. Tungsten filament lamps of various shapes and sizes. The light from these contains a greater proportion at the red end of the spectrum and less at the violet end compared with daylight. Areas of the salon in tungsten light will have a warmer appearance as a result.
3. Fluorescent lamps are mostly straight tubes but ring-shaped tubes are also manufactured. The range of white lights available usually includes one to match tungsten light (warm white), one to match daylight and one that includes more blue/violet and less red than daylight (cold white).

From the choices listed above the following suggestions are made:

1. Area used for day make-up – natural daylight or daylight fluorescent lamps.
2. Area used for evening make-up – filament or warm white fluorescent lamps.
3. Reception and other areas of the salon where a warm relaxing atmosphere is desirable – filament or warm white fluorescent lamps.
4. Epilation and other activities where a sharp contrast between light and dark is required – cold white fluorescent lamps.

Care should be taken to avoid the problem of *glare* in any lighting system. This is caused by the eyes looking directly at a very bright concentrated light source. The chief culprit in the salon will be a clear glass tungsten lamp where the hot filament can be seen. This can be avoided by using a lamp with a diffusing coating on the inside of the bulb, known often as a pearl bulb. Clear bulbs can be used but they should be surrounded by a suitable lamp shade. Use of spotlight bulbs in reception to accentuate an advertising display should be carefully thought out to avoid the risk of them shining directly into clients' eyes.

Questions

1. For what purpose in a beauty salon would you use (a) a convex mirror, and (b) a convex lens? Explain why.
2. What would be the colour of (a) red lipstick, (b) blue eyeshadow, and (c) white face powder when seen in (i) daylight, (ii) sodium street light and (iii) red disco light?
3. Describe the action of light on varnished nails resulting in a red and glossy appearance.
4. (a) Why cannot normal-sighted people see clearly objects closer than 25 centimetres?
   (b) Why are images seen in a clear glass cupboard door?
   (c) What safety hazard is associated with the presence in the salon of magnifying lenses?
5. State the advantages and disadvantages of using fluorescent lamps to illuminate a salon.

Part 2
Cosmetic products

Chapter 6

Care of the skin

The chief function of cosmetic products is to enable us to present an attractive appearance to our fellow human beings and, as a result, to generate a state of satisfaction and assurance in ourselves. Since the largest area of our body that we expose to society is our skin, the care of this important organ has a high priority in beauty therapy.

Structure of the skin

Although the thickness of the human skin never exceeds 2·5 mm and is in some places only 0·5 mm, it has a definite structure, being divided into two main layers:

1. The dermis, containing blood vessels, nerves and glands.
2. The epidermis, or outer layer, where only that part of it next to the dermis contains living cells (see Fig. 6.1), the remainder consisting of layers in various stages of keratinisation (conversion to keratin). Keratin is a very tough protein ideally suited to its role of acting as a barrier keeping out our external environment. Nails and hair are made of the same material.

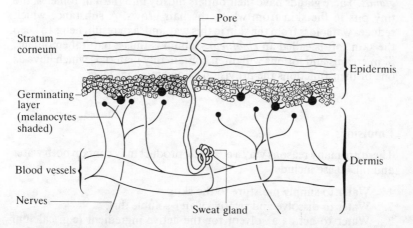

Fig. 6.1 Section through the skin

The surface of the skin (stratum corneum) is continually being lost due to rubbing against other objects and flaking, so there must be a constant replacement process going on. This is performed by the deepest layer of the epidermis (germinating layer) where cells undergo division creating new material for the layers above. Special cells are also found in this layer called *melanocytes* whose function is to manufacture *melanin*, the pigment which protects us from ultra-violet waves and results in a sun-tan (see Ch.19).

The sweat glands (eccrine glands) are to be found within the dermis over most of the surface area of the body and they are connected to this surface by ducts whose openings are the pores in the skin. The aqueous (watery) solution of salts and organic compounds that they secrete passes through these ducts and flows on to the skin surface. The water in the secretion evaporates from the surface, leaving behind the dissolved solids. This evaporation has a cooling effect on the skin (see Ch.1) and assists in regulation of body temperature.

Emollience

Apart from sweat secretion, there is also a loss of water by evaporation from the epidermis itself, and this must be replaced by water from the blood vessels in the dermis, otherwise the skin will lose its softness and smoothness. A soft skin will need to hold 10 per cent of its own weight as water. Most skin care creams will contain water which can be absorbed by the skin for this purpose. Another way to conserve water in the epidermis is to make it more difficult for it to evaporate from the surface. This can be done by applying an oily layer over the skin through which the water finds it more difficult to pass (see Fig. 6.2). This is one of the functions of *sebum*, the oily substance secreted by the *sebaceous glands*. These glands have their outlets mostly into the hair follicles, the tiny pits in the skin from which the hair grows. A substance which reduces water loss from the skin in this way and, as a result, helps to keep the skin soft is called an *emollient*. Sebum is thus a natural emollient. Skin creams and lotions will often contain oily materials which have as one of their functions the provision of an emollient layer.

Emulsions

There are many reasons why a cosmetic product may contain both water and oil. These include:

1. Water to supply moisture to the skin.
2. Water to dissolve and remove water-soluble dirt.
3. Water to act as a solvent for the active ingredient (e.g. calcium thioglycollate in a chemical depilatory).

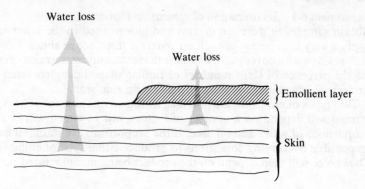

Fig. 6.2 Action of an emollient

4. Water to produce a cooling effect by evaporation.
5. Oil to act as an emollient.
6. Oil to dissolve and remove oil-soluble dirt.
7. Oil to act as a solvent for the active ingredient (e.g. vitamin E in skin-nourishing creams).
8. Oil to act as a barrier layer.
9. Oil to act as a lubricant.

Since water and oil molecules are chemically very different in structure (see Ch. 11) they are unable to mix (*non-miscible*). Placed together in the same container, they will form separate layers. The oil, being less dense, floats on top of the water. By stirring, shaking or some other way vigorously attempting to mix the two layers, one of the liquids (or *phases*) will break up into tiny drops and be dispersed in the other (see Fig. 6.3). Such an arrangement is called an *emulsion*. Many cosmetic creams and lotions are emulsions although the drops are very small and can only be seen under a microscope.

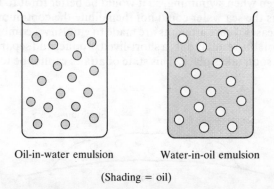

Oil-in-water emulsion   Water-in-oil emulsion

(Shading = oil)

Fig. 6.3 Structure of an emulsion

Experiment 6.1   Examination of creams and lotions

Obtain samples of different creams and lotions used in the salon and apply a very thin smear of each on separate microscope slides. Cover each smear with a cover glass. Examine the smears under the microscope for the presence of large numbers of similar shaped droplets (seen as circles). This will indicate if the product is an emulsion.

Two types of emulsion are possible, as shown in Table 6.1. The type formed will depend on a number of factors, one of which will be the proportions of water and oil used. If the proportions are similar it may be possible by varying conditions to produce either type of emulsion. The choice will then depend on the product being manufactured.

Table 6.1   Emulsions

Type of emulsion	Dispersed phase	Continuous phase
Oil-in-water (O/W)	Oil	Water
Water-in-oil (W/O)	Water	Oil

Since the continuous phase makes contact with the skin more easily than the dispersed phase (see Fig. 6.4) it will have the more rapid action on the skin. A moisturising cream would be more effective if water were the continuous phase (O/W emulsion), but a massage cream would be more lubricant if oil were the continuous phase (W/O emulsion). A water-in-oil emulsion, however, would give the skin a greasy appearance, as it is the light reflected off the surface of the continuous phase that is received by the observer's eyes (see Ch. 5). Such an appearance would not be acceptable for a cream to be left on the skin in the daytime. Again, an emulsion can be diluted only by adding more of the liquid which forms the continuous phase. This means a cream that is an O/W emulsion can be removed by water, provided the water in the cream has not evaporated. A sun-tan cream, however, should preferably stay on the skin even when swimming, so it would be better for it to be a W/O emulsion as the sea water could not then dilute the continuous phase.

In most cases where attempts are made to emulsify a combination of water and oil the result is only a short-lived product and separation into two layers soon takes place. This state of affairs cannot be tolerated in

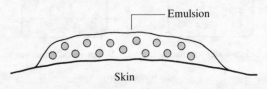

Fig. 6.4 Emulsified product on the skin

commercially-produced cosmetics, since the customer would need to shake or stir before, and perhaps during, its use. Two methods are used to produce a permanent emulsion, both of which may be used in the same product. These involve adding to the emulsion other compounds known as *emulsifiers* and *stabilisers*.

Emulsifiers form a surface layer on the tiny drops of the emulsion shielding them from contact with the liquid of the continuous phase (see Fig. 6.5 (a), (b)). This will have the effect of reducing the forces trying to separate the two non-miscible liquids. The drops will then more easily remain dispersed. See Chapter 12 for a more detailed description of emulsifier action.

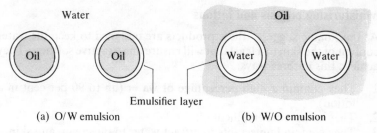

Fig. 6.5 Shielding action of an emulsifier

Experiment 6.2 Emulsifiers

In a number of test-tubes place approximately equal volumes of water and an oil such as olive oil, and add to each test-tube a small quantity of a substance that you think might act as an emulsifier. Try washing-up liquid, shampoo, soap solution, lecithin and glyceryl monostearate. Shake each tube vigorously and then allow to stand. Absence of separate layers and an opaque product indicate an emulsion has been formed.

Stabilisers are compounds dissolved in the continuous phase which increase its viscosity. This makes it more difficult for the dispersed drops to move about and come close enough to one another so that joining-up, or coalescing, may take place. This would be the first step towards forming a separate layer. When water is the continuous phase, the stabiliser is usually a compound with a large molecule, known as a *hydrocolloid*, which may need special treatment to persuade it to form a solution. Starch powder, for example, needs to be stirred into a little cold water first before hot water can be added to take it into solution. Starch, proteins, gums and water-soluble plastics such as polyvinyl pyrrolidone may be used as stabilisers.

Humectants

Just as the water in a cream may evaporate when it is spread over the skin surface, so can there be a loss of water from such a product when it is in the container in which it is sold. This will occur especially when the lid or cap is removed to use the cream. Loss of water can result in a deterioration of the product which will have an adverse effect on future sales. To counteract this, manufacturers may include in the product a substance that attracts water vapour from the atmosphere. Such substances are called *humectants*. They will also help indirectly in the supply of water to the skin when the cream is applied, as they will help to maintain the reservoir of water held in the cream. Common humectants include glycerol, sorbitol and glycols. See Chapter 10 for a more detailed explanation of their behaviour.

Moisturising creams and lotions

As their name suggests, these products are designed to keep the water content of the skin to a level that will ensure an attractive softness. They achieve this in three ways:

1. They contain a high percentage of water (up to 90 per cent in a lotion).
2. They contain an emollient oil.
3. They contain humectants to attract water to the cream and skin.

When these products are applied to the face as the basis of the make-up, the term *foundation cream* may then be used. Foundation creams must have good powder-holding properties and this is achieved by increasing the humectant content, or by adding lanolin. They may also be pigmented.

A cream used on the face in the day should not look greasy, as this would not produce a fashionable appearance, and because of this they are sometimes called *vanishing creams*. To avoid a greasy effect O/W emulsions are used and the emollient chosen has a high melting point so that it is not liquid at skin temperature. Stearic acid, a fatty acid, has been used for this purpose although a fatty alcohol, cetyl alcohol, and certain waxes that form tiny crystals in the solid state are more modern alternatives. If stearic acid is used, a base such as potassium hydroxide or sodium hydroxide may be included during manufacture. This will react with some of the fatty acid to form a soap which will then act as an emulsifier. The emulsifying action of soap is considered in Chapter 12.

Skin conditioning creams

These are the creams that are normally applied to be left on the skin overnight, especially those for the face. Known also as *emollient creams*, they usually have a high oil content and, as a greasy appearance is not a problem at night, may be W/O emulsions. They soften the skin by being highly emollient, not by being a source of moisture. They do not have to rub in well but should not be easily removed by contact with bedclothes.

Skin nourishing creams contain additives such as vitamins or hormones dissolved in either the water phase or the oil phase of the emulsion. There is still very little scientific evidence that these substances are easily absorbed by the skin, especially oil-soluble compounds. It also seems doubtful, on the evidence available, whether any such absorption would have a noticeable effect on skin condition. In other words, the *efficacy* of such creams would be regarded as low.

Claims made for the beneficial effects on the skin of essential oils are usually based on the wrong interpretation of the word 'essential'. These oils got their name from the pleasant smell, or essence, which they produce on evaporating. They are in no sense compounds which the skin needs for its metabolism but can act as a preservative to the cream. Vitamin E is a popular additive to nourish the skin but it is also known to have anti-oxidant properties, and it may be as a preservative that this vitamin functions in such creams. Nutritionally, vitamin E has not been shown conclusively to be an essential ingredient of the human diet.

Cleansers

These products are an alternative to the use of a detergent such as soap together with water on the facial skin. Their function is to remove old make-up and other forms of soil present including sebum and the water-soluble solids left behind by sweat. They may be, quite simply, a water-free mixture of oils and waxes and, as such, take the form of a non-viscous lotion. Such products will only remove oil-soluble soil. Cleansing creams and milks, however, will usually be an emulsified product able to remove water-soluble soil also.

Mineral oils (see Ch. 11) are better solvents of oil-soluble compounds than vegetable oils and they will account for a large proportion of the composition of the cleanser (up to 50 per cent). A cleansing cream with only mineral oil as its oil phase, however, would prove to be too drying on the skin as it would remove all natural sebum. To counteract this, a small proportion of vegetable or animal oils is included. The choice of oils will also be determined by the need for the cleanser to be easy to spread over the skin and to be easy to remove afterwards.

Present-day manufacturers of cosmetics have a wide range of emulsifiers to choose from for their formulations but this was not always so. The original cleansing cream formulation, still used by some manufacturers, made use of the fact that beeswax contains some free (uncombined) fatty acid in its composition. The wax was included as part of the oil phase, and borax, an alkaline salt (see Ch. 10), was dissolved in the water phase. On emulsifying, the borax reacted with the fatty acid from the beeswax to form a soap which then acted as the emulsifier. A similar production of emulsifier during manufacture was seen in some moisturising creams. Creams made to the beeswax/borax formulation often contain sufficient water to have a cooling effect when applied to the skin, and are then known as *cold creams*.

Skin toners

The use of a toner following skin cleansing is normal make-up practice. Their main function is to produce a tightening of the skin, sufficient to reduce the size of the sweat gland duct openings, or pores. They do this chiefly by evaporating from the skin and again producing cooling. To achieve this they contain a volatile liquid such as common alcohol, but other ingredients which have a tightening, or *astringent*, effect may be dissolved in the liquid. An example of such a substance is witch hazel. Because the liquids used in toners are also oil solvents, they are also claimed to be preventers of excessive oiliness, and would certainly remove any cleansing oil that remained.

Hand care creams and lotions

Much of the care given to the skin of the hands will be similar to that given to the face. In the daytime a moisturising product can be applied, while at night a higher oil-content emollient cream can be used. Since the skin of the hands comes into closer contact with the environment than that of other parts of the body, it may be considered necessary to apply a layer of cream on the skin surface before carrying out a particular task, e.g. washing crockery, floors, cars, etc. Such a cream is known as a *barrier cream* and will be formulated according to the purpose for which it is being used. Mineral oils form the best oil barrier against water but it is difficult to find a substance to protect the hands against detergents since they will tend to remove a barrier oil.

Experiment 6.3 Preparation of a hand cream
The following formulation makes an easily emulsified emollient hand cream:

1.	Lanette emulsifying wax	14·0 g	⎫
2.	White lanolin	4·0 g	⎬ (A)
3.	Glycerol	5·0 ml	⎭
4.	Water	76·0 ml	⎫ (B)
5.	Preservative	1 microspatulaful	⎬

Weigh and measure out ingredients A into a plastic beaker or other suitable container and then place on a water-bath at 75°C. Dissolve the preservative in the measured quantity of water in a second container and place this on the same water-bath. When ingredients A have melted together, remove both containers from the water-bath. Now add B to A gradually over one minute, stirring continuously with a glass rod. The use of a plastic container for A at this stage avoids consequent scratching and possible cracking of a glass beaker. Continue stirring until a stable emulsion is formed. Add perfume to mask the lanolin smell when the temperature is below 40°C.

Acid creams

The skin's normal condition is to present a slightly acid (pH 5·0 to 6·0) surface to the outside world due mainly to the secretions found on it. This helps to prevent the multiplication of harmful (or pathogenic) bacteria there. A number of products that come into contact with the skin, however, tend to be alkaline. This is true of even the mildest of soaps as explained in Chapter 12. In order to return the skin to normal condition after such contact, some manufacturers now market so-called *acid-creams* or *pH balanced creams*. These are often for use as the foundation for facial make-up. The pH balancing is carried out by compounds known as buffers (see Ch. 10). Most hair conditioners are formulated to perform a similar function on the hair after the alkaline processes of perming, tinting and bleaching.

Massage creams

These creams are used chiefly as a lubricant between the therapist's hands and the client's skin. Their composition will be largely determined by the type of massage for which they are intended and the individual therapist's preferences, but they are normally high-oil-content creams. Since they will be removed after the massage, a greasy-looking W/O emulsion can be used to hold the oil.

Questions

1. What is the difference between an emollient and a humectant?
2. Describe, with the aid of a diagram, the structure of an emulsion. Compare the actions of the emulsifier and the stabiliser in an emulsion.
3. Explain the use of the terms moisturising, foundation and vanishing used to describe a pre-makeup cream for the face.
4. Mineral oils are used in preference to vegetable oils in certain types of skin cream. Give reasons.
5. What is the function of the: (a) eccrine glands;   (b) sebaceous glands;   (c) natural acid condition of the skin's surface?

Chapter 7

Personal hygiene products

Being exposed to the environment, our skin easily becomes the resting place for a variety of substances with which it makes contact. There is a limit to the amount of build-up of these substances that our modern standards of hygiene will tolerate, and consequently the cosmetic industry finds a demand for products to absorb and remove these.

Sources of skin dirt

Dirt, or soil (to use the less emotive term), found on the skin will arise from a number of sources including:

1. Natural secretions from the sweat and sebaceous glands.
2. Old unwanted make-up.
3. Substances floating around in the air and present on many surfaces (e.g. dust and pollen).
4. Substances left on the skin, especially the hands, as a result of some activity.

Types of dirt

When cleaning is being considered, dirt is classified under three headings:

1. *Soluble dirt.* This includes all material soluble in water such as the residue from dried-up sweat, certain types of makeup, salt from sea-bathing and sugar dust.
2. *Greasy dirt.* This includes sebum, oil-soluble make-up and fats from handling foodstuff.
3. *Particle dirt.* This includes all solid materials that do not dissolve in water such as garden soil, pollen and various micro-organisms.

Detergency

The dictionary definition of the word 'detergent' is 'a substance which cleans'. If all skin dirt came under the heading of soluble dirt then cleaning would be no problem provided adequate supplies of water were available. Water would be the only detergent needed.

To remove greasy dirt and the particle dirt which is usually adhering to it we can make use of a grease solvent. This is the method used in cleansers (see Ch.6) and also in the dry-cleaning of clothes, wigs, etc. Suitable liquids may be found for this purpose but they often prove to be flammable and they may give off a toxic vapour. No such problems exist when using water to clean, so there is a demand to be able to use it for all cleaning purposes. To make this possible, compounds are added to the water so that it can also remove greasy and particle dirt. It is these compounds that are normally referred to as detergents. Detergents assist water to clean, and they carry out their action in three stages:

1. They lower the surface tension of the water so that it can then spread over the skin surface and penetrate all its irregularities. This process is called wetting.
2. With the assistance of some form of agitation such as rubbing by the hands, they effect the removal from the skin of greasy and particle dirt.
3. They keep the particles of dirt suspended in the wash water so that they are lost down the waste-pipe during rinsing.

The third stage in this process involves having tiny drops of grease dispersed in water and is reminiscent of the structure of an oil-in-water emulsion. We say the detergent must keep the removed dirt emulsified. This suggests that detergents and emulsifiers must be similar compounds. Chapter 12 gives a more detailed discussion of this topic.

Experiment 7.1   Detergents as wetting agents
1. Take a number of small beakers and fill them about three parts full with tap water. Add a teaspoonful of talcum powder, chalk or kaolin to each. Note how the powder floats on the water due to surface tension. To each beaker add about 5 ml of detergent-containing products such as shampoo, bubble bath and washing-up liquid using a medicine spoon. Notice how the powder now sinks to the bottom.
2. Place a small amount of tap water in the palm of an unwashed hand and notice its tendency not to spread. Add a few drops of shampoo to the water and note how this promotes the spreading on the skin.

Soaps

As the original detergents, members of the soap family have probably been in use for centuries. Since the raw materials required to produce them are fat or oil and some form of alkali, they could conceivably have been first made by accident when melted animal fat met the potassium carbonate in hot wood-fire ashes. Nowadays hard soap in tablet or flake form is made using the alkali, sodium hydroxide, while soft soap is made from potassium hydroxide. A by-product of this process is glycerol which finds an important use as a humectant in cosmetics (see Ch. 6). It is not recovered in soft soap manufacture, so is still present in the gel as dispensed to impart its water-attracting properties to the product.

Experiment 7.2   Disadvantages of soap
Using pure soap flakes designed to wash delicate garments, or shavings from a tablet of mild soap, make up a solution using hot distilled or de-ionised water. Prepare four test tubes containing:

1.   a few drops of universal indicator solution.
2.   a flake of fused calcium chloride dissolved in half a tube of distilled water.
3.   a pinch of ordinary salt dissolved as in 2.
4.   a pinch of citric acid dissolved as in 2.

Add soap solution till three parts full to each tube and note the result. You will need a colour chart to interpret the result of 1.

From Experiment 7.2 the disadvantages of only using soap as detergent are shown to be that:

(a) even the purest of soap gives an alkaline solution in water;
(b) soap produces insoluble scum in hard water;
(c) soap is not very soluble in salty water such as that of the sea;
(d) an insoluble precipitate is formed in the presence of an acid.

A chemical explanation of these reactions is given in Chapter 12. With the development of chemical knowledge in the twentieth century, alternative detergents have been developed and these have largely replaced soap in cosmetic products because they do not suffer from the above disadvantages. A detergent which is not a soap is called a *soapless detergent*, and these are looked at in more detail in Chapter 12.

Shampoos, bath and shower products

A shampoo is a cleaning cosmetic associated with the washing of hair. The name originated in the sub-continent of India and was derived from the pressing action used in massaging the scalp during the washing process. A modern shampoo is basically a solution of a soapless detergent in water but other ingredients are often present, as shown in Table 7.1.

Experiment 7.3   Preparation of a liquid shampoo
The preparation can be easily carried out in a 400 cm³ glass beaker or similar container. The formulation is as follows:

1. Triethanolamine lauryl sulphate   150 cm^3
2. Water   100 cm^3
3. Sodium chloride   7·5 g
4. Colour and perfume as desired

Table 7.1 Composition of a shampoo

Ingredient	Function
Water	Solvent for other ingredients
Soapless detergent	To assist water to clean hair
Auxiliary detergent	To act as a foam stabiliser
Thickening agent	To prevent spillage and run-off from the head
Organic acid	To reduce pH to match that of the hair and scalp
Opacifier	To give a 'richer' appearance to the product
Other additives	To give colour, perfume, medicating properties, etc.

Weigh out the salt and place in the beaker. Add the water and stir till the salt has dissolved. Measure out the detergent and add this to the salt solution. Stirring should now produce a more viscous solution to which the colour and perfume may be added.

Foam-bath or bubble-bath products are very similar in composition to shampoos. Their chief ingredient is a soapless detergent to have a cleaning action on both the bather's skin and the bath inside surface. It is obviously important that the foam produced should be sufficiently stable to last for most of the bathing time, but that it should not make emptying the bath a difficult process. Since it is still customary not to rely on them for completely cleaning the skin but to use soap also, they must be able to maintain their foam in the presence of soap. This presents problems in the choice of detergent and foam stabiliser and is still not completely resolved. The use of soap is best delayed till near the end of the bath-time when its foam-collapsing effect can be used to facilitate emptying.

Bath salts and cubes do not normally contain a detergent. Their principal ingredient is a water-softening compound which dissolves in the bath water. Colour and perfume are added and the latter persists throughout the time of bathing. Sodium carbonate or washing soda can be used for softening but it is a salt which produces quite strongly alkaline solutions which are harmful to skin protein. Its crystals are not particularly attractive in shape and they tend to crumble as they lose water to the atmosphere. A mixed crystal of sodium carbonate and bicarbonate, known as *sodium sesquicarbonate*, has a much more attractive feathery appearance and is to be preferred for bath salts.

With the rapid spread of the use of a shower as an alternative to bathing has come the demand for a cleaning product to replace tablet soap. There is always a period of time between initial wetting and final rinsing when the body is subjected to the cooling effect of the water evaporating from the skin surface. Producing sufficient lather for soaping-over from a tablet of soap prolonged this time. Modern *shower-gels* are already in liquid form and can be more rapidly applied. They may be based on soap or a soapless detergent but have the viscosity of the product increased to a gel structure which makes them easier to apply without spillage or waste. The use of larger molecule compounds to increase viscosity has already been referred to in Chapter 6 when stabilising an emulsion. A further development has been to combine hair shampoo and shower gel in one product as a *whole-body shampoo*.

Apocrine gland secretion

Reference has already been made in Chapter 6 to the more common type of sweat gland, or eccrine gland. The human body also has within the skin a second type of gland known as an *apocrine gland*. These occur mainly in certain areas notably in the axilla, groin, anal and genital regions and around the nipples. Unlike the eccrine glands, they discharge their secretion into hair follicles. They are thought to have had a secondary sexual function early on in human evolution. This is supported by the observation that they are most active between puberty and menopause in women.

The secretion contains proteins, lipids and lipoproteins which are not found in eccrine secretion. It is doubtful whether the secretion itself has an offensive smell, or malodour, but on reaching the hair follicle the compounds contained serve as a source of nutrient for bacteria present. As a result of the bacterial metabolism, waste products are produced which are responsible for so-called *body odour*.

Deodorants and antiperspirants

There are two personal hygiene problems associated with the secretion from the apocrine glands. These are:

1. The production of underarm odour.
2. The appearance under the arms of wet patches on clothing and the possible fabric-rot resulting.

Deodorants, as their name suggests, are cosmetics designed to prevent the odour problem. The active ingredient in them is a compound which either prevents the bacteria responsible from multiplying (a *bacteriostat*), or actually destroys the bacteria present (a *bactericide*). Hexachlorophene was used for this purpose until recently but it has been found to produce certain side-effects and has been largely replaced by *hexamethylene tetra-amine*. It may be included in a lotion or cream but is not very effective in a powder owing to the small area of contact with the follicle surface.

Antiperspirants have the function of preventing excessive perspiration but it should be remembered that they are only applied under the arms, so will have no significant effect on the body's ability to lose heat by evaporation of sweat. It was originally thought that the compounds used in them had an astringent effect on the skin which resulted in a reduction in the diameter of the orifice of the gland duct. In this way the rate of flow was reduced. The current view is that their effect is to increase the permeability to the secretion of the wall of the duct. This has the effect that some of the secretion passes into the surrounding tissues with a smaller volume reaching the follicle.

The active ingredient of an antiperspirant is often a salt of aluminium. Such a salt will normally give an acid pH in aqueous solution (see Ch. 10), but if the simpler salts such as sulphate or chloride are used, the pH is too low, resulting in irritation and possible fabric rot. Instead, *alumimium chlorhydrate* is included which gives a pH of 4. Antiperspirants are manufactured in a number of forms including aerosols, roll-on applicators and sticks. The choice of base materials for these needs to be made with care as the active ingredient is a strong electrolyte.

EEC regulations for the cosmetic industry place an upper limit on the amount of a bacteriostat or bactericide that may be included in a product. If odour prevention is the main objective for a person with an excessive secretion problem, this may not be possible by using a deodorant only as it would require above limit amounts of bacteria-controlling compounds. To solve this, cosmetics containing both deodorant and antiperspirant are produced, the deodorant coping with the odour from a reduced flow of secretion.

Talcum powder

The main purpose for which talcum powder is used is to absorb sweat and sebum, and to prevent chafing between different parts of the skin surface as they rub together. If applied after bath or shower it will also absorb water remaining behind after towelling. If perfumed, it can also assist in preventing odour problems. Talcum powders are a mixture of at least three powdered solids including:

1. a good absorber,
2. a substance that allows skin surfaces to slide freely by each other,
3. a substance that helps the mixture to stick to the skin.

Experiment 7.4 Absorbent properties of powders
Mount a burette vertically in a stand with its jet several centimetres above the surface of a sheet of glass or a ceramic tile. Fill the burette with water and zero. Measure out 1 g of powder and place it on the glass or tile. Run a few drops of water at a time on to the powder and mix in with a spatula or glass rod. Continue adding water drop by drop until a

creamy consistency is produced in the sample. Note the volume of water added. The powders chosen should include chalk, kaolin, rice starch and magnesium carbonate if available, and may be repeated using a thin oil in place of water to represent sebum.

The results of Experiment 7.4 will indicate a good compound to include in a talcum powder for absorbency. Chalk and magnesium carbonate that have been produced in a very finely-divided form by precipitation generally score well here. By far the best compound to prevent chafing is *talc*, or magnesium silicate, and it will probably account for as much as 70 per cent of the talcum powder composition. It is mined in Italy, France and India but may often contain tetanus spores as a result of this. Consequently all talc used in cosmetics must be steam-sterilised before use. Although the word 'talc' is often used as an abbreviation for 'talcum powder' on labels and packaging, it should be noted that there is a substance whose common name is talc but which is only one ingredient of talcum powder. The adhesive properties of the powder are conferred on it by including a small percentage of magnesium stearate or zinc stearate. Being insoluble salts of a fatty acid, they stick to the skin.

Experiment 7.5   Preparation of a talcum powder sample
Weigh out carefully 35·0 g of sterilised talc, 2·5 g of precipitated chalk and 2·5 g of zinc stearate, adding each in turn to a clean yogurt or cream carton. Seal the top of the carton with a lid or film of wrapping material and shake vigorously for fifteen minutes. A little perfume may be added during this time.

Foot and baby powder

These cosmetics are specialised forms of talcum powder and so have additional functions. Since the feet spend much of the day enclosed in shoes, sweat will tend to accumulate on them. This may result in soreness, especially between toes, a greater possibility of odours and there may be a tendency to encourage fungal growth producing problems such as athlete's foot. Foot powders will, therefore, contain a greater proportion of absorbent than normal body powders and manufacturers will include anti-bacterial and anti-fungal compounds.

Baby powders are normally designed for use at nappy-change times, so there will again be a need for increased absorbency. Urea present in the urine will be converted to ammonia by bacteria present on the skin and this alkaline substance may be the cause of nappy rash. A bacteriostat is included in the powder to prevent excessive ammonia production. Boric acid was used freely for this purpose but there are now restrictions, as it has been found to penetrate the baby's skin and reach the blood system.

Questions

1. What are the three categories of dirt? Give an example in each case of a product used in the beauty salon which might be present in the dirt on the therapist's skin after a day's work.
2. What are the disadvantages of using soap as a detergent?
3. Explain what is meant in cosmetics by the following terms: (a) opacifier; (b) bactericide; (c) antiperspirant.
4. Where might you expect to find the following compounds used in cosmetics: (a) sodium sesquicarbonate; (b) magnesium stearate; (c) magnesium silicate; (d) hexamethylene tetra-amine?
5. What are the differences between the apocrine glands and the eccrine glands?

Chapter 8

Care of the nails

One important service that the beauty salon will provide for its clients will be the expert skill of the make-up artist. Attention will be paid to the appearance of the nails, lips, eyes and of the face in general. In this chapter we look at the cosmetics used on the nails, taking them in the sequence in which they would be applied during a salon manicure.

Structure of nails

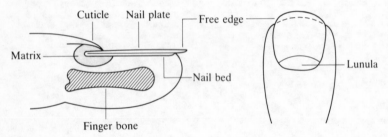

Fig. 8.1 The nail on its finger

The nail, like the skin, is made of keratin and grows as a development of skin structure (see Ch. 6). It is the *nail plate* which requires the attention of the manicurist's scissors and files. This consists of horny cells like the stratum corneum and has its root in the matrix. It grows away from this towards the free edge without restriction in length. The plate is attached along most of its length to the nail bed which is now thought to grow with it. Underlying the cells of the nail bed are many nerve endings which are responsible for the sensitivity of the nails to external pressure. A flap of skin overlaps the matrix and part of the nail plate and is referred to as the *cuticle*. The so-called 'half-moon' or lunula at the bottom of the nail separates the nail bed from the matrix.

Cuticle remover

Since the nail cuticle may grow over the nail base, tending to obscure the lunula and thus to spoil the shape of the nails, it is often necessary to remove some of it during manicure. Cutting is not always to be recommended so chemical attack is employed instead.

Chemical cuticle remover makes use of the ability of an alkaline substance to break down the structure of protein. *Potassium hydroxide* in amount up to 5 per cent is often the active ingredient but milder preparations may include an alkaline salt such as *sodium phosphate*. These are applied in solution in water or a water/alcohol mixture. Care should be taken not to allow these potent products to touch other parts of the skin or clothing. To assist the manicurist in this the solution may have a thickening agent added, or it may be supplied as a cream. Alkalis can also remove oil from the nails using the soap-making reaction referred to in Chapter 7. To counteract this degreasing effect, glycerol may be included in the remover, or *cuticle cream* may be applied. This cream, which is also used to soften the cuticle before removal, will be an emulsified product containing emollients.

Nail creams

Just like the skin itself, the nail requires the presence of water to keep it soft. It will become brittle otherwise and easily broken or split. Nail creams will, therefore, be very similar in composition to the skin conditioning creams discussed in Chapter 6. They will be emulsions containing water, humectants and emollients.

Nail hardeners

These are products painted on to the nails which have a strengthening effect, making them a good base for application of varnish. Sometimes the active ingredient is an astringent metallic salt such as those used in antiperspirants which tighten up the nail structure. Other products include a formaldehyde resin which forms a layer on top of the natural structure. Formaldehyde resins have been known to act as sensitisers, resulting in serious side effects in the surrounding skin. When hardeners containing these are to be applied, a layer of oil placed on the skin of the finger around the nail beforehand is to be recommended.

Nail white

The free edge of the nail does not transmit light from the nail base and so has a more translucent appearance. This gives an off-white top border to the nail which may be emphasised and whitened by using nail white. Two compounds often included in cosmetics for their whiteness are zinc oxide and titanium oxide. In nail white they are prepared either as a suspension in water or incorporated in the wax base of special pencils.

Nail polishes

The contours of the nail plate surface are often irregular and need to be smoothed before putting on varnish. This is done by using a suitable abrasive powder, known as a buffing powder, or incorporating the powder in a wax pencil. Talc, kaolin and chalk are satisfactory abrasives, but the best buffing material has been found to be the more expensive *stannic oxide*.

Nail varnish

The final stage in nail make-up is to apply a film of material on the surface of the nail plate which will have certain characteristics. These are given in Table 8.1. Bearing in mind the requirements given for the

Table 8.1   Characteristics of a good nail varnish

Film characteristics	Required varnish property
Even thickness	Medium viscosity with good flow and wetting action
Good gloss	Varnish should dry with a smooth surface
Good adhesion	Dissolved material should stick to nail
Flexibility (to prevent cracks or chipping)	Varnish must contain a plastic material
Quick drying	Volatile solvents to be used
Uniform colour	Pigment to be finely ground and well dispersed

varnish in the table, there will normally be *four* components in a clear nail varnish as follows:

1. A film former – usually *nitrocellulose.*
2. An adhesive substance – usually a synthetic resin.
3. A plasticiser – usually a non-volatile solvent.
4. A mixture of solvents – to dissolve the other three components.

If a formaldehyde resin is used as adhesive it may give rise to an allergic reaction as mentioned in connection with nail hardeners. The mixture of solvents used must be carefully chosen in order to achieve an acceptable drying time. This time will be decided by the properties of the liquids chosen and the proportions in which they are mixed. *Ethyl acetate*, *butyl acetate* and *toluene* are used but they may be diluted with other liquids which are not solvents for the other components of the varnish. This is done to reduce costs.

When more than one layer of varnish is applied in the salon:

1.   Base coats have a greater resin content to stick to the nails, and a greater proportion of the volatile solvent, ethyl acetate, to dry rapidly. They are made less viscous by reducing the nitrocellulose content, and contain less plasticiser to give a harder film.

2. Top coats contain more nitrocellulose and plasticiser to give a good gloss, but less resin since adhesion to earlier coats is easier than to the nail itself.

Coloured varnish will contain a suitable pigment either inorganic or derived from a dye as discussed in Chapter 13 and, if a pastel shade is required, white titanium oxide. Pearlescent effects may be achieved by adding guanine a complex chemical obtained naturally from the scales and body of certain fish, although there are alternative materials available such as bismuth oxychloride.

Nail varnish removers

These can be obtained in two forms. They are either a simple mixture of solvents which can rapidly dissolve off the old film, or they can be produced as emulsified creams. The simple solvents tend to be very degreasing on the nails, especially *acetone*, and may have an oil such as lanolin added to them to reduce this effect. The cream removers will obviously have oil in the oil phase of the emulsion.

Therapists are not recommended to use the mixture of solvents in a remover to reconstitute a dried-up bottle of varnish. Even if this is successful, the resulting salvaged product is unlikely to have a tolerable drying time as the mixture of solvents used in a remover can be quite different from that used in the varnish. Whether using varnish or remover, the therapist should not forget that both are flammable products and should be handled with care.

Nail repair products and false nails

Damaged finger nails can be repaired by products available from industry. One such product attempts to provide a coating compatible with the keratin of the nails by including further keratin combined with cellulose nitrate in a suitable volatile solvent mixture similar to that used for nail varnish. Other compounds may be included to improve adhesion, flexibility, water resistance and gloss of the resultant film. This keratin-containing product is also an aid to achieving artificial nails.

An alternative nail repair cosmetic contains fine fibres such as those from rayon mixed with an adhesive film-former and a solvent. Like nail varnish, the film-former is preferably nitrocellulose to which may be added a synthetic resin and a plasticiser. The solvents again are quick-drying and include ethyl acetate, butyl acetate and toluene.

Rather than use the keratin-containing product discussed above, artificial nails and nail elongations may be produced by forming a type of plastic, known as a *polymer*, with the assistance of catalysts supplied with the product. The nail elongation is formed by applying, successively, first a liquid containing a compound whose molecules can link up to form a polymer, and then the powdered catalyst. This process is repeated until the required build-up is obtained. Methyl methacrylate is often the polymer-forming compound. In common with all the products dealt with in this section, an opacifier or pigment may be added if required.

Questions

1. The formulation for a cuticle remover includes (a) potassium hydroxide, (b) water, (c) glycerol and (d) a thickening agent. Explain the function of each ingredient.
2. Why must care be taken in the use of (a) cuticle remover, (b) nail hardener and (c) nail varnish remover?
3. There are two manicure cosmetics that may contain titanium oxide. What are these and what is the function of the oxide in each product?
4. What ingredients would you expect to find in clear nail varnish? How would you expect the proportions of these to vary when comparing a base coat and a top coat?

Chapter 9

Cosmetics for the face

There is little doubt that the part of the human anatomy which expresses personality the most and leads to attraction between one individual and another, both within and across the sexes, is the face. The need to take care of the skin becomes especially important, therefore, when the face is considered, and it is here also that make-up can enhance the appearance and consequent attraction. Many interesting types of cosmetics are used to this end.

Face packs and masks

These facial skin-care cosmetics are applied as liquid or paste and allowed to dry or set while in position. They:

(a) have a transient astringent effect as they shrink on to the face;
(b) have a warming effect by interfering with skin respiration which may result in excessive sweating. They are then said to be *diaphoretic*;
(c) may have a cleansing effect if they contain absorbent materials, or if skin debris, etc. sticks to them as they are removed.

The combined warming and tightening may produce stimulation and rejuvenation. A good face pack should be smooth to apply and dry rapidly with shrinking. Whilst in place it should not have an objectionable odour for the client, and, although it should adhere to the skin, it should be easy to remove without causing pain.

The most well-known face mask is the *clay-based* or earth-based type. It consists of a paste of absorbent solid material supplied either to be mixed or ready-mixed. Kaolin is a popular base for these masks. It is mined as china clay, but can also be made in a colloidal form. Fuller's earth and volcanic bentonite are also used for their good absorbency. The paste shrinks as it dries out and then acts as a good skin cleanser. Many improvements have been made in this type of mask since its first introduction. Any materials obtained from the ground are now sterilised before use as they may contain spores of pathogenic bacteria. The modern mask has no odour and contains bleaching and whitening additives to improve its appearance. The particles of the clay material are kept in suspension by thickening agents and a plasticiser, such as glycerol, is added to make the paste easier to apply.

Wax masks are put on the face as a liquid at a temperature just above 37°C but they set on contact. As wax is not pervious to water, these masks prove to be very diaphoretic and flush out the sweat gland ducts. Skin debris sticks to the wax as it is removed. The mask may contain mineral oil which improves the spreading properties.

Rubber-based masks applied as a latex emulsion dry as they lose water. The waterproof properties of the rubber remaining makes them very warming but they are easy to remove by stretching. Vinyl-based masks have been developed as an alternative to rubber. They use water-insoluble vinyl resins such as polyvinyl acetate. Absorbent solids can be incorporated in them to improve the cleansing action.

Masks based on *hydrocolloids* prove to be easy to apply and quick to dry but they are not very cleansing. Hydrocolloids are compounds with large molecules such as those used to stabilise an emulsion, and include starch, proteins, gums and water-soluble plastics. They are either applied to the face in aqueous solution which gels as it loses water, or as a prepared gel which must be melted before application. The mask dries as the gel loses its water content.

Cleansing, toning and moisturising

We have seen considered in Chapter 6 the composition and action of the cosmetics used in these three important stages that precede make-up. There we saw use being made of the good oil solvent properties of mineral oils to remove grease during cleansing. Volatile products, often containing ordinary alcohol, then follow as we improve skin tone. Finally a moisturising cream uses its three ways to keep skin soft by containing water, emollient and humectant. This latter cream then forms the foundation for make-up.

Blushers

Blushers are a form of coloured make-up designed to be applied to the cheeks to give the same impression as that seen when a natural blush occurs due to some event, comment, etc. The natural blush is the result of dilation of the blood vessels in the skin and is therefore red in colour. Since the French word for red is *rouge*, this is the name by which blushers were originally known.

A pigment or dye (see Ch. 13) will form the essential coloured ingredient in the blusher, but this can be carried in a number of different bases. Compact blusher will have the colour mixed with the ingredients used in face powder (see later in this chapter) and then pressed in the form of a solid cake. A cream blusher may have the colour suspended in a mixture of waxes and oils, or present in one of the phases of an emulsion. Liquid rouge contains a dye dissolved in water to which a thickening agent and a wetting agent have been added. A stick blusher will be wax based and have a composition similar to lipstick (see later in this chapter).

Face powder

A face powder will consist of a mixture of several white powdered ingredients to which colour may be added. The properties which a good face powder must have are shown in Table 9.1. A number of compounds

Table 9.1   Face powder properties

Property	Explanation
Covering power (or opacity)	The ability to hide minor skin defects and blemishes
Absorbency	The ability to absorb sweat, sebum and any excessive oil from the foundation
Slip	The ability to spread easily and to leave a smooth feel
Bloom	The ability to produce a matt surface
Adherence	The ability to stick to the skin

are available from both mineral and synthetic sources to help provide these properties in the powder and they are listed in Table 9.2.

Table 9.2   Face powder ingredients

Chemical name	Common name	Covering power	Absorbency	Slip	Bloom	Adherence
Titanium oxide		*				
Zinc oxide		*				
Calcium carbonate	Chalk		*	+	*	
Magnesium carbonate			*			
Silica			*			
Aluminium silicate	Kaolin	+	*			
Magnesium silicate	Talc			*		
	Rice starch		+	+	*	
Magnesium stearate				+		*
Zinc stearate				+		*

*Exhibits this property very well.
+Exhibits this property moderately

A typical face powder formulation would be as follows:

Talc	64 per cent
Kaolin	20 per cent
Precipitated chalk	5 per cent

Zinc oxide	5 per cent
Zinc stearate	5 per cent
Magnesium carbonate	1 per cent
Colour and perfume	As required

Translucent powders contain more zinc oxide and less titanium dioxide than opaque powders.

Experiment 9.1   Investigation of face powder ingredients
Try to obtain samples of as many as possible of the compounds in Table 9.2 and examine them by touch, feel and appearance to see how the properties required in a face powder are exhibited by them. In some cases you may find that the manner in which they have been made or mined will influence their properties. The label on the container or the manufacturer's catalogue may assist you here.

Lipstick

Traditional lipsticks are dispersions of colour in a base which makes the stick. They should have an attractive appearance when on sale with a smooth wet-looking surface uniformly coloured. This appearance should be retained during shelf and usage life. Ingredients should be harmless to the skin and if ingested. They should be easy to apply and remove when required. The film they leave on the lips should not be either too greasy or too dry, and the colour should not change while being worn.

The colouring material used is part dye (to stain the lips) and part pigment (to give surface cover). The most common dyes used are the so-called *bromo-acid dyes*, while the pigment may be organic or inorganic in origin. As in the case of nail varnish, titanium oxide may be included to give a more pastel shade. A number of ingredients make up the *stick base*. These are:

1. Waxes to give hardness.
2. Lanolin to give emollience.
3. Petroleum jelly for lubrication and spreading.
4. Castor oil to act as the dye solvent.

This mixture of base materials must soften on contact with the skin and should not transfer easily during a kiss. If perfume is to be added its taste should be considered as well as its smell.

Eye make-up

Since the human eye is a very delicate sense organ, it is necessary to restrict severely the type of coloured material that can be included in eye make-up. Vegetable colours such as chlorophyll and the insect-derived dye, cochineal, are sometimes used. It is more common, however, to employ inorganic pigments such as the various coloured forms of iron oxide, chromium oxide, manganese oxide and titanium oxide. Coloured chromates, cobalt salts and ultramarine may also be included. The colour can be compounded in a variety of base materials. These take the form of:

1. Pencils and sticks with a hard wax base.
2. Cakes with a softer soap and wax mixture base.
3. Creams with an oil/wax or emulsion base.
4. Liquid products which are water or water/alcohol suspensions.

Mascara can be purchased in cake, cream or liquid form, *eyeshadow* as stick, cream or liquid and *eyeliner* in the form of a cake. *Eyebrow pencils* have their colour in a wax base similar to lipstick.

Irritants and sensitisers

Many of the compounds found in modern cosmetics are new to the human species. When they arrive on the skin, the presence of a 'foreign' substance triggers off what is known as the *triple response*. This consists of an initial reddening of the skin due to dilation of the veins, swelling due to loss of fluid from the veins and finally extreme reddening due to dilation of the arteries. The response follows the liberation of histamine in the skin as a result of the invasion of the cosmetic compound. It is the body's method of defending itself.

If that compound produces the response when it is first applied to the skin, it is called an *irritant*, but if there is no response until the second and subsequent applications, the compound is called a *sensitiser*. Sometimes irradiation by electromagnetic waves, such as ultra-violet waves, can assist the compound in the cosmetic to produce the triple response. Such a compound is referred to as a photosensitiser. A person with an allergy for a certain compound already has the necessary antibodies in the blood to repel the invader before it is used on the skin. Colours and perfumes used in cosmetics often act as irritants or sensitisers, and must be suspected if the triple response occurs.

Questions

1. Compare three types of face mask, paying special regard to (a) ease of application and removal, (b) action as an astringent, (c) diaphoretic effect and (d) cleansing action.
2. What is meant by the terms 'slip' and 'bloom' as applied to a face powder? A certain face powder contains 60 per cent talc. What would be the effect of reducing this to 30 per cent, and replacing the

remainder by equal parts of magnesium carbonate and titanium oxide?

3. Why are there greater restrictions in the use of dyes and pigments in lipstick and eye make-up compared with their use in blusher?

4. In which cosmetic would you expect to find (a) fullers earth, (b) polyvinyl acetate, (c) castor oil and what would be their function? Different cosmetics may be chosen for each substance if necessary.

Part 3
The ingredients of cosmetics

Chapter 10

Acids and associated compounds

In Part 2 we met in name only the various ingredients found in cosmetics. Often these are compounds whose chemistry is linked with the family of compounds called acids. This chapter aims to give the enquiring therapist a deeper understanding of the behaviour and relationship between such associated compounds.

Properties of acids

If a person with little knowledge of chemistry is asked what sort of substance an acid is, they will probably use the word corrosive or burning in their description. These words, however, only apply to certain powerful acids such as that found in car batteries (sulphuric acid). The majority of acids are quite mild in action and some even safely form an essential part of the diet. Ascorbic acid, for example, is vitamin C. Others are included in cosmetics without harm to the skin as we saw stearic acid being used in a vanishing cream (Ch. 6). Table 10.1 shows acids classified under three headings. The word 'organic' used there means a compound whose molecules contain atoms of carbon.

What then is the property that links all acids? This can best be explained by considering hydrochloric acid. It has molecules consisting of one atom of hydrogen and one atom of chlorine linked together by a single chemical bond and shown symbolically as

$$H - Cl$$

The hydrogen atom only contains one proton (positive) but the chlorine atom contains seventeen. The electrons (negative) in the molecule therefore experience a greater attraction towards the chlorine atom. When hydrochloric acid molecules dissolve in water their hydrogen protons break away to form separate particles known as *hydrogen ions* and these carry a positive charge. The presence of water molecules is essential for this process to occur. Although most other acids have a more complex molecular structure, they will contain at least one hydrogen atom in a similar situation to the hydrogen atom in the hydrochloric acid molecule.

We can state, therefore, that acids are compounds which produce

Table 10.1   Acids

Type of acid	Examples
Strong acids	Sulphuric acid
	Nitric acid
	Hydrochloric acid (in the stomach)
Weak organic acids	Citric acid (citrus fruits)
	Acetic acid (vinegar)
	Lactic acid (tired muscles)
Fatty acids	Stearic acid (derived from animal fat)
	Oleic acid (derived from olive oil)
	Butyric acid (derived from butter)

hydrogen ions on making contact with water. It is this ability to form hydrogen ions that enables acids to react chemically with other materials, so producing new substances. In cosmetics we are chiefly concerned with their reaction with bases and alcohols.

Bases and alkalis

In chemistry a base is a compound that reacts with an acid to form a salt and water, and we show this in a chemical statement thus:

$$\text{Base + acid} \longrightarrow \text{salt + water}$$

There are different types of bases, but the ones that will be considered here are *metal oxides*, such as zinc oxide, and *alkalis*, such as potassium hydroxide. Metal oxides are not soluble in water but may react chemically with it to form an alkali. Alkalis are soluble in water and in it form separate ions. One of these is called a *hydroxyl ion* and is found in all alkali solutions. It carries a negative charge.

Unlike acids, there are no weak alkalis and they are able to react strongly with many materials including proteins, fats, glass, synthetic fibres and aluminium. The therapist should always treat products containing them with care. Cuticle remover, hair relaxers and wash-basin waste pipe cleaners are often alkali-based.

pH scale

When an acid is dissolved in water the acidity of the solution produced will depend on the number of hydrogen ions present. This number will be determined by:

1.   The quantity of acid dissolved,
2.   The type of acid dissolved, since all the molecules of a strong acid produce ions but only a proportion of weak acid molecules do so.

If an alkali is added to an acid solution, the hydroxyl ions will tend to combine with hydrogen ions from the acid to produce water molecules thus:

Hydroxyl ion (negative) + hydrogen ion (positive) ⟶ water molecule

This will have the effect of reducing the acidity of the solution. If just sufficient alkali is added to give equal numbers of hydroxyl and hydrogen ions the solution is said to be *neutral*. If more alkali is now added, the solution will have an alkaline reaction.

To express precisely the acidity or alkalinity of a solution a number scale is used, known as the pH scale. pH means power of hydrogen ions, and the scale is illustrated in Fig. 10.1. There is a mathematical reason for the numbers chosen but this will not be dealt with here.

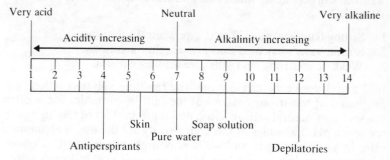

Fig. 10.1 The pH scale

Dyes can be found which change colour if the pH of the solution changes. They are known as *indicators*. A solution containing several of these goes through a series of colour changes with change in pH from 1 to 14. These colour changes are similar to those seen in the light spectrum (see Ch. 5). The solution is known as universal indicator and papers impregnated with it are called pH papers.

Experiment 10.1 pH testing
Using pH papers and a suitable colour chart test any cosmetics available in the salon to find out their acidity or alkalinity. Follow the manufacturer's instructions for the use of these papers. Moisten the palm of the hand with a little distilled water and use a pH paper to measure the skin value. Wash the hands with soap and test again both before and after rinsing with distilled water.

Salts

These are compounds that can be formed by adding a base to an acid. For example:

1.   Zinc oxide + stearic acid ⟶ zinc stearate + water
2.   Potassium hydroxide + citric acid ⟶ potassium citrate + water

The name of the salt is obtained from the name of the base and acid that could be used to produce it. In most cases the 'ic' of the acid is converted to 'ate' in the salt name, with certain exceptions. Hydrochloric acid has salts called chlorides, and sulphuric acid has salts called sulphates. Not all salts are soluble in water but those that are exist in the form of ions when in the solution. Because ions are electrically charged, a compound whose molecules ionise is called an *electrolyte*. Acids, alkalis and salts fall into this category.

Acidic and alkaline salts

A solution of a salt in water does not always have a pH of 7·0. The value obtained will depend on which base and acid could be used to produce it. Thus:

1.   Strong base/strong acid salts give neutral solutions.
2.   Strong base/weak acid salts give alkaline solutions.
3.   Weak base/strong acid salts give acidic solutions.

In 2 and 3 above we can say that the resulting solution reflects the properties of the strong 'parent' of the salt. In cosmetics use is often made of non-neutral salts to avoid making a product of too high or of too low a pH. Examples of this seen already are the use of aluminium salts in antiperspirants and sodium phosphate in cuticle remover. Aluminium oxide is a weak base and phosphoric acid is a weak acid.

Experiment 10.2   pH of salt solutions

Take a number of test tubes and half fill with distilled water. Now add a small quantity of a salt to each tube and shake or stir till dissolved. Test each tube with a piece of pH paper and note the results as indicated by the colour chart. Salts to try could include sodium chloride (common salt), sodium carbonate (washing soda), potassium nitrate (saltpetre), sodium borate (borax) and aluminium chloride.

Buffers

When a manufacturer wishes to produce a cosmetic with a certain pH, he or she will want to make sure that the product maintains this value when on sale and when in use. This will be especially true in the case of cosmetics with a pH well away from neutral such as antiperspirants and depilatories (see Fig. 10.1). An accidental change of pH towards very acid or very alkaline could have a serious effect on the part of the body where it was applied. To prevent this happening the manufacturer will make use of a *buffer* in the product concerned.

A buffer consists of a mixture of one of the acidic or alkaline salts referred to in the previous section together with either its acid or its base. If an acidic salt is used, such as ammonium chloride, it will be mixed with a weak base such as ammonium hydroxide, but if an alkaline salt is used, such as potassium citrate, it will be mixed with a weak acid such as citric acid.

Let us take the potassium citrate/citric acid mixture to explain buffering action. Potassium citrate molecules will be completely ionised in aqueous solution, but citric acid, however, is only partially ionised in such a solution. so in the buffer mixture there will be:

(a) many potassium ions from the salt;
(b) many citrate ions from the salt and acid;
(c) some hydrogen ions from the acid;
(d) many unionised molecules of the acid.

Suppose the cosmetic product in which the buffer is used tends to become more acidic. This will mean that for some reason more hydrogen ions are being produced. In the presence of the buffer mixture they will combine with citrate ions to form more citric acid molecules and so the pH of the product will remain under control. On the other hand, if the product tends to become more alkaline this could mean an increase in hydroxyl ions, but these will combine with hydrogen ions from the buffer mixture to form water molecules. Some more of the citric acid molecules will then ionise to provide more hydrogen ions and thus restore the pH to its original value.

The choice of a weak acid/salt buffer mixture or a weak base/salt buffer mixture will depend on the pH value of the product to be controlled. A different mixture would be chosen to buffer an antiperspirant from that used to buffer a chemical depilatory.

Alcohols and esters

Another group of compounds made use of in cosmetics which also react chemically with acids is the *alcohol* family. Common alcohol, which we meet in alcoholic drinks, methylated spirits and astringents, is the most well-known member of the family and has for its chemical name, *ethanol*. Glycerine, known to chemists as *glycerol*, is also an alcohol. Many alcohols have chemical names ending in 'ol'.

Since ethanol can be used to make alcoholic drinks, its manufacture and sale are controlled by customs regulations. It is however a very good solvent and is used extensively in cosmetic manufacture, as for example in the compounding of perfumes. It is made by fermentation of sugar and by other methods and has to be distilled to separate it from the water mixed with it. This makes it an expensive product. It is often sold in a *denatured* form with another alcohol mixed with it. For many purposes the presence of another alcohol has no disadvantages but it does render the mixture undrinkable, and so satisfies customs regulations. Two such denatured mixtures are:

1. Industrial methylated spirits (95 per cent ethanol + 5 per cent methanol)
2. Denatured alcohol (97½ per cent ethanol + 2½ per cent isopropanol)

The reaction between alcohols and acids can be expressed as follows:

$$\text{Alcohol} + \text{acid} \longrightarrow \text{ester} + \text{water}$$

and looks similar to the reaction between bases and an acid, but esters have very different properties from those of salts. They do not ionise in water and the majority are not even soluble in water. Waxes, most animal and vegetable oils, nail varnish solvents and certain of the ingredients used to produce the odour of a perfume are esters.

Experiment 10.3   Making an ester
Take 5·0 cm³ of industrial methylated spirits in a boiling tube, add to it 3·0 cm³ of glacial acetic acid followed by a few drops of concentrated sulphuric acid (**handle carefully!**). Warm the tube in a water bath for about ten minutes and then pour the tube contents into a large container of cold water. Note the pleasant smell of the ester formed by the reaction:

$$\text{Ethanol} + \text{acetic acid} \longrightarrow \text{ethyl acetate} + \text{water}$$

This ester is used as a solvent in nail varnish.

Humectants

In Chapter 6 we saw how certain compounds are added to creams to ensure that they do not readily lose water to the atmosphere on exposure to it. Such compounds we call humectants. They are introduced again here because the most popular humectants used by manufacturers are members of the alcohol family.

Water molecules contain an atom of oxygen to which two atoms of hydrogen are bonded, but, instead of being arranged symmetrically on opposite sides of the oxygen atom thus:

$$\text{H—O—H}$$

investigation by X-rays has shown the arrangement to be as in Fig. 10.2. Since the oxygen atom contains more protons than both hydrogen atoms together, all the electrons of the molecule tend to congregate at the oxygen end. This end thus takes on a negative charge leaving the opposite end positively-charged. Because of this we say that water

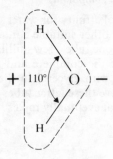

Fig. 10.2 Arrangement of atoms in a water molecule

molecules are *polar* molecules. They will be attracted to any other particle that is electrically-charged. This is how water helps an acid molecule to ionise.

A characteristic of an alcohol molecule is the presence in it of a group of atoms known as a hydroxyl group. This group consists of one atom of oxygen bonded to one atom of hydrogen thus:

$$—O—H$$

The oxygen atom can form an additional bond which links the group to the rest of the molecule. The structure of the molecule of simple alcohols like ethanol can be represented as shown in Fig. 10.3. Such a structure will also be polar in its behaviour and will be able to attract water molecules to itself.

The alcohols chosen by manufacturers for inclusion in cosmetics as humectants are usually those with more than one hydroxyl group in the molecule. Glycerol, for example, has three such groups. This gives more positions to which water molecules may be attracted and so increases humectancy.

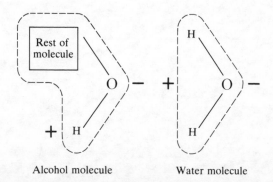

Alcohol molecule   Water molecule

Fig. 10.3 Attraction of water by humectant alcohol

Experiment 10.4   Alcohol affinity for water

Take three test tubes, or other suitable containers, and about half-fill each with water. Add to one tube a few millilitres of ethanol, carefully shake or stir and notice the complete and rapid mixing of the two liquids. Repeat this test with glycerol in the second tube and liquid paraffin in the third. Leave these latter tubes standing for several days and note how the glycerol eventually mixes with the water but the oil never does.

Questions

1.   Explain what is meant in science if a cosmetic is said to contain an organic acid. Give examples of such acids and their sources.
2.   What problems might arise if a chemical depilatory of pH 12·0 were manufactured and sold in glass containers?
3.   Why could sodium acetate be used as part of a buffer mixture? What would be the other ingredient and how would the mixture control pH?
4.   Explain how glycerol could be used (a) to make an ester, and (b) as a humectant.
5.   What is meant in science by the terms (a) base, (b) electrolyte and (c) polar molecule?

Chapter 11

Oily compounds

The compounds met in the previous chapter are, in the main, those found in the aqueous part of a cosmetic. We have seen in Part 2, however, the important role played by oils and waxes in creams and lotions, and their action on the skin. In this chapter we study the chemical structure and the varying properties of the oily compounds used for this purpose.

The hydrocarbon chain

It is easier to understand the different molecular structures of oily compounds if we first get to know what arrangement of atoms endows a molecule with oily properties. Investigation of the molecules of substances with such properties, both those found naturally and in synthetic products, shows that somewhere in the structure will be what is called a *hydrocarbon chain*. As its name suggests, it consists only of a string of hydrogen and carbon atoms as shown in Fig. 11.1. It is this chain that is the 'fingerprint' of oiliness. These chains will be very long in many fats, oils and waxes, often containing between ten and twenty carbon atoms or more. Notice how hydrogen atoms only form one chemical bond, as they do in water molecules, but carbon atoms form four bonds each. The bonds are shown as short straight lines in the figure.

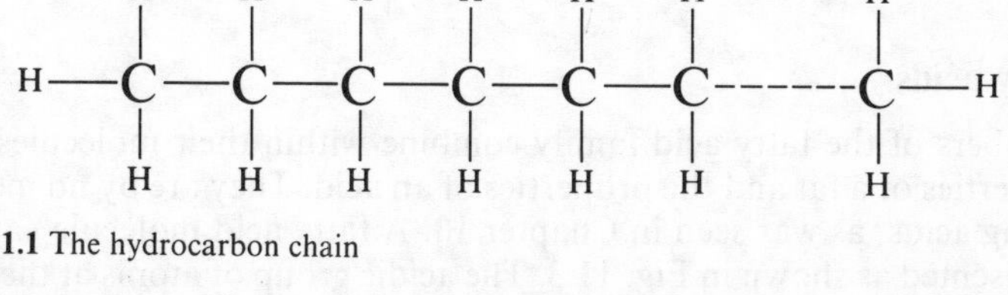

Fig. 11.1 The hydrocarbon chain

Since the atoms in a molecule occupy the three dimensions of space, and not a flat surface as depicted in Fig. 11.1, the 'backbone' of the chain is not straight but kinked, its direction changing at each carbon atom. To recognise this fact and to produce a simpler representation in a diagram, the chain is often shown as in Fig. 11.2. It is assumed that at each end and at each kink there is a carbon atom, that neighbouring atoms are joined by a single chemical bond and all bonds not being used to form the backbone have hydrogen atoms attached. Use will be made of this representation in the rest of the book.

Fig. 11.2 Representation of a hydrocarbon chain

Mineral oils

Crude oil, or petroleum, obtained from under the ground all over the world is a complex mixture of compounds, many of which are hydrocarbons. Their molecules are built up from hydrogen and carbon atoms only. The crude oil is taken to a refinery where it is heated under controlled conditions. As different temperatures are reached, different fractions of the oil vaporise and these vapours are led away by pipes to cooler regions where they condense back to liquids. This process is called fractional distillation, and from it we get the well-known products of the refinery including petrol for cars, paraffin oil used for heating and the mineral oils used in cosmetics. These include *petroleum jelly*, *paraffin wax* and *liquid paraffin*, the latter not to be confused with paraffin oil.

Mineral oils are often chosen in preference to vegetable oils by cosmetic manufacturers because:

(a) they are better grease solvents;
(b) they are less viscous and sticky;
(c) they are less likely to go rancid;
(d) they are less likely to be contaminated with micro-organisms;
(e) they are less occlusive because they remove natural sebum from the skin.

Fatty acids

Members of the fatty acid family combine within their molecules the properties of a fat and the properties of an acid. They are by no means strong acids, as was seen in Chapter 10. A fatty acid molecule can be represented as shown in Fig. 11.3. The acidic group of atoms at the end of a long hydrocarbon chain only accounts for a small proportion of the total number of atoms making up the molecule. In stearic acid, for example, the hydrocarbon chain contains seventeen carbon atoms and thirty-five hydrogen atoms but the acidic group contains only four atoms. It is not surprising that such acids can be used in cosmetics as part of the oil phase as an alternative to other fats or waxes (see Expt 11.1).

Fig. 11.3 Fatty acid molecule

Fatty acids often have names revealing the fat or oil from which they can be manufactured including:

(a) oleic acid from olive oil;
(b) palmitic acid from palm oil;
(c) butyric acid from butter;
(d) linoleic acid from linseed oil.

Fatty alcohols

In Chapter 10 we saw that the alcohol family of compounds always have at least one hydroxyl group in their molecules. This is true of the fatty alcohols whose molecular structure can be represented as shown in Fig. 11.4. Like the fatty acids, the molecule is largely a hydrocarbon chain with a small terminal two-atom group at one end. The longer the chain, the greater the departure in properties from those of ethanol and the more the fatty chain properties predominate (see Expt 11.1).

Fig. 11.4 Fatty alcohol molecule

The terminal hydroxyl group still exhibits polar properties and this is often made use of in cosmetics when a fatty alcohol, such as *cetyl alcohol*, is included as a bridging substance between water and oil. The hydroxyl group is attracted to water but the chain is attracted to oil. In this role it behaves as a secondary emulsifier (see Ch. 12).

Experiment 11.1 Physical examination of fatty acids and alcohols
Obtain samples of stearic acid and cetyl alcohol and add a little of each to water in separate test tubes. Note how each shows little desire to dissolve in water. Rub a sample of each between finger and thumb and note their waxy feel.

True waxes

In Chapter 10 we referred to the reaction between alcohol and acid which resulted in the formation of a compound known as an ester. If the alcohol is a fatty alcohol and the acid a fatty acid, the resulting ester is called a *true wax*. We can represent the reaction thus:

Fatty alcohol + fatty acid ⟶ true wax + water

The true wax molecule will contain two hydrocarbon chains from its parent alcohol and acid. The hydroxyl group of the alcohol and the acidic group of the acid will react to form the link producing water as a by-product. Thus the true wax molecule can be represented as in Fig. 11.5. Effectively, the molecule will have the structure of a very long hydrocarbon chain and this will account for the high melting point of the wax.

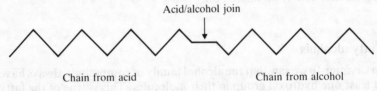

Fig. 11.5 True wax molecule

The term true wax is used to distinguish these esters from paraffin wax, which is not an ester. The melting point of the wax will depend on the alcohol and acid of which it is the ester. Waxes are used in cosmetics as the base of many stick or pencil products and are also added to the oil phase of a cream to raise its melting point and reduce the chance of a greasy appearance at skin temperature.

Triglycerides

The most common fats and oils derived from animal and vegetable sources consist of a mixture of compounds known as triglycerides. In Chapter 10 we saw that glycerol is an alcohol with three hydroxyl groups in each molecule. It is often represented as shown in Fig. 11.6. Because of this structure it can form esters with acids and, in particular, fatty acids. Since *three* fatty acid molecules can link with each glycerol molecule, the resulting esters are the triglycerides (See Fig. 11.6). Since many different fatty acids are known and the acid molecules linking with the glycerol molecule can be:

1. three the same,
2. two the same, one different,
3. all different,

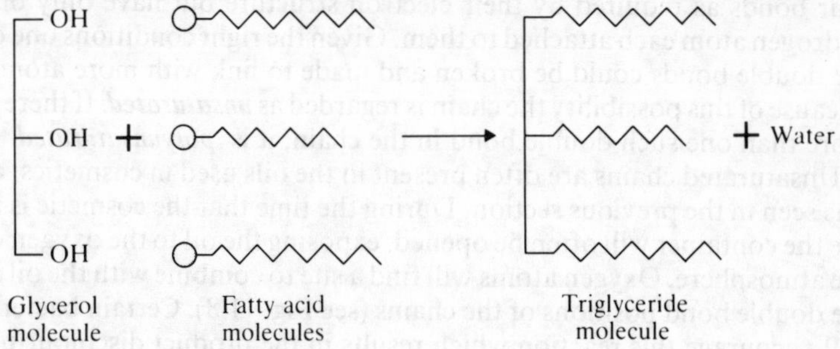

Fig. 11.6 Formation of a triglyceride

a large number of triglycerides is possible. This is why natural fats and oils are mixtures. The types and proportions of the different triglycerides present determine the physical and chemical properties of the oil or fat.

One important property when these oils are used in cosmetics will be the temperature at which they soften. Since they are mixtures they will not have a definite melting point, but it is necessary to know if they cease to be a hard solid at skin temperature. They will be easier to apply if this is so. If a triglyceride contains hydrocarbon chains from *unsaturated* fatty acids it will increase the likelihood of the oil being soft, or even liquid, at skin temperature.

Saturated and unsaturated compounds

The hydrocarbon chain found in oily compounds was depicted in Fig. 11.1 and showed carbon atoms linked by single chemical bonds. All the other bonds to the carbon atoms were made with hydrogen atoms. There was no possibility of additional atoms joining on to the chain. Such a structure is said to be *saturated*. (Compare this with a solution of salt in water which cannot dissolve any more solid and is also said to be saturated.)

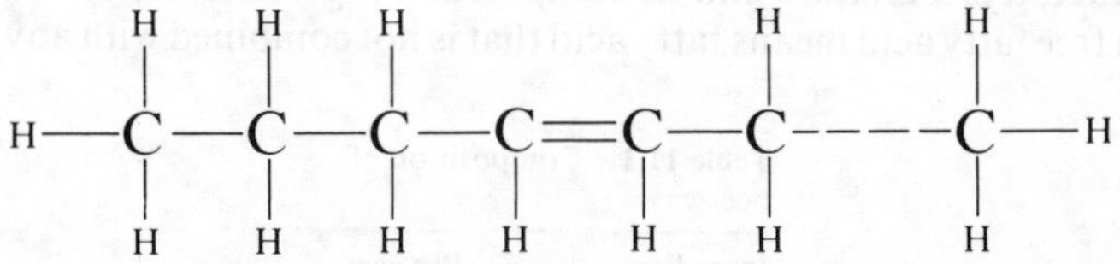

Fig. 11.7 Unsaturated hydrocarbon chain

In Fig. 11.7 we see a hydrocarbon chain which has a double bond between two carbon atoms. These particular carbon atoms are forming four bonds as required by their electron structure but have only one hydrogen atom each attached to them. Given the right conditions one of the double bonds could be broken and made to link with more atoms. Because of this possibility the chain is regarded as *unsaturated*. If there is more than one such double bond in the chain, it is *polyunsaturated*.

Unsaturated chains are often present in the oils used in cosmetics, as was seen in the previous section. During the time that the cosmetic is in use the container will often be opened, exposing the oil to the oxygen of the atmosphere. Oxygen atoms will find a site to combine with the oil at the double bond positions of the chains (see Fig. 11.8). Certain bacteria will encourage this reaction which results in the product discolouring, thickening and eventually becoming rancid. In order to prevent this an antioxidant will be added to the cosmetic (see Ch. 15).

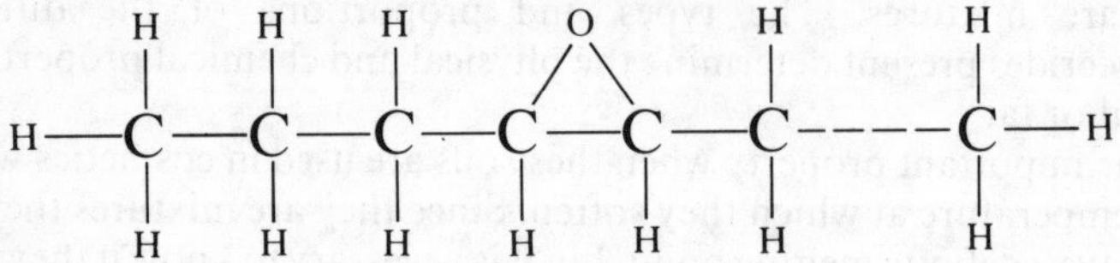

Fig. 11.8 Oxidation of an unsaturated chain

Paraffin wax, beeswax and lanolin

These three non-synthetic products find many uses in both cosmetics and in salon treatments. Paraffin wax is one of the fractions emerging from the distillation process at oil refineries. It is a mixture of mainly hydrocarbons of different-sized molecules and its softening temperature range can be varied by adjusting the composition of the mixture. This proves very convenient when employing it for waxing treatments in the salon. A wax which had to be at a high temperature to remain molten could not be applied to the skin without causing damage and pain to the client.

Beeswax is manufactured by bees to build the honeycomb structure in which the honey is stored. As might be expected for such a natural product, it is a mixture and its composition is given in Table 11.1. The term free fatty acid means fatty acid that is not combined with any other

Table 11.1 Composition of beeswax

Ingredient	Per cent
True waxes	71
Free fatty acids	14
Hydrocarbons	12
Other ingredients	3

substance to form, for example, salts or esters. Their presence in the beeswax is made use of in the traditional recipe for the manufacture of cleansing creams when alkaline borax is allowed to convert some of the fatty acid to soap, which then acts as the emulsifier (see Chs 6 and 12). Cosmetics containing beeswax may need to be perfumed in order to mask the beeswax smell. Most of the fatty acid present, including that which is part of the true wax esters, is saturated, so rancidity is not a great problem.

Lanolin is the equivalent of human sebum and acts as the water-proofing material on the wool of sheep. It is also known as wool wax, or wool fat. Its composition is shown in Table 11.2. The main reason for its popularity as a component of skin creams, lipstick, etc. is its ability to act as an emollient. An explanation of why such material should have this property is still not clear but, apart from the free alcohols present, most of the fatty acid chains in the esters also have hydroxyl groups attached to them and we have seen in Chapter 10 how such groups can be water-attracting.

Table 11.2 Composition of lanolin

Ingredient	Per cent
True waxes and cholesterol esters	73
Free fatty alcohols	25
Other ingredients	2

Lanolin-containing cosmetics sometimes produce allergic reactions when applied to the skin. The raw product may also impart an odour to the cream in which it is incorporated, and may require masking. The components in the natural mixture are also separated into fractions and used as such by manufacturers as an alternative.

Experiment 11.2   Softening temperature of waxes
Obtain samples of different paraffin waxes, beeswax, depilatory wax, etc. and place sufficient in separate boiling tubes to half-fill when molten. Label one of the tubes and then place it in a pre-heated water bath. Bring the temperature of the water up to boiling point and allow it to simmer. When the wax has melted insert a suitable thermometer and remove the tube to a draught-free enclosure. A conical flask serves this purpose well. With a stop-watch or clock take the temperature at half-minute intervals until the wax has completely solidified. By plotting a graph of temperature (y-axis) against time (x-axis), or by simply inspecting the readings taken, the softening range can be determined. This will be the temperature when the rate of cooling was slower, or even stationary. By repeating the experiment with the other samples, softening ranges can be compared.

Questions

1. Give an example of a fatty acid and a non-fatty acid and explain why they have some similar and some differing properties.
2. In which type of skin cream would you expect to find (a) a mineral oil and (b) lanolin? Explain why.
3. Olive oil is liquid at room temperature but does not have a definite freezing point. Give possible reasons for these facts.
4. Why are true waxes and triglycerides considered to be esters? How do they differ in chemical structure?
5. What is meant by the term 'unsaturated fat'? Why might such a fat be incorporated in a cosmetic? What problem might this lead to and how could it be avoided?

Chapter 12

Emulsifiers and detergents

The importance of an emulsifier in allowing water and oil to remain in close proximity to each other in a cosmetic cream has already been referred to in Chapter 6. In Chapter 7 the final function of a detergent in helping water to clean was found to be that of keeping greasy and particle dirt emulsified in the wash water. When we come to look at the chemical structure of emulsifiers and detergents we should not be surprised to discover that they are similar substances. Many compounds can be used for both purposes, but whereas all detergents can act as emulsifiers, the reverse is not true.

Structure of an emulsifier molecule

The formation of a barrier layer of emulsifier molecules surrounding the tiny drops of an emulsion was shown in Fig. 6.5, and it can be seen that in both types of emulsion the emulsifier molecules have to be in contact with water at one end and with oil at the other. Within the emulsifier molecule, therefore, there must be an arrangement of atoms which likes water (*hydrophilic*) and another that likes oil. An arrangement that likes oil is likely to dislike water (*hydrophobic*).

In Chapter 11 the chemical fingerprint of oiliness was found to be a hydrocarbon chain and this atomic arrangement is also found in emulsifier molecules. The chain is often referred to as the molecule's hydrophobic tail because the geometry of a hydrocarbon chain is reminiscent of that of an animal's tail. For hydrophilic properties we need to refer to Chapter 10. Here we saw that water molecules are polar in character. They have a positive and a negative end and so an arrangement of atoms that carries an electrical charge will be attracted to water. This is the situation in one part of an emulsifier molecule and, because it is usually small compared with the hydrophobic tail, it is referred to as the molecule's hydrophilic head. Figure 12.1 shows how the whole molecule is represented in diagrams. Some emulsifiers ionise in water just like other electrolytes. One of the two types of ions formed will include in its structure the hydrophobic tail. Emulsifiers which ionise with the hydrophobic tail in the negative ion are said to be *anionic*, those with the tail in the positive ion are said to be *cationic* (see Ch. 4).

Non-ionic emulsifiers have a polar group of atoms for their hydrophilic head. Fatty alcohols fit into this category.

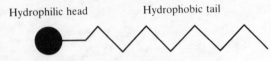

Hydrophilic head   Hydrophobic tail

Fig. 12.1 Emulsifier molecule

Explanation of detergent function

The type of molecule that makes a good detergent will be similar to that of an emulsifier and its general structure can be used to explain the stages of the cleaning process described in Chapter 7.

1. Lowering of the water surface tension

A water molecule away from the surface in the main body of the water is completely surrounded by other similar molecules and is attracted by them equally in all directions (see Fig. 12.2 (a), (b)). These forces, therefore, balance out. A molecule which is part of the surface, however, has no neighbouring molecules to one side so it experiences an unbalanced force trying to pull it inwards away from the surface. This results in the surface of any water sample being in a state of tension.

Introduction of detergent to a sample of water will result in some detergent molecules moving to occupy space in the surface. By doing this their hydrophobic tails may project out of the water they dislike. This desire to be in the surface will help to counteract the forces trying to pull water molecules inwards and will cause a fall in surface tension.

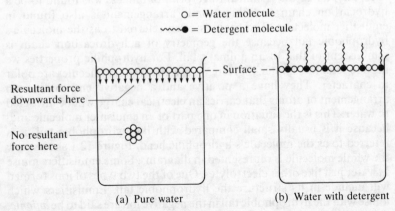

O = Water molecule
∿● = Detergent molecule

Resultant force downwards here

No resultant force here

(a) Pure water   (b) Water with detergent

Fig. 12.2 Surface tension reduction by a detergent

2. Removal of greasy and particle dirt from a surface

Another place where detergent molecules may get their tails out of water is on the surface of grease droplets and dirt particles (see Fig. 12.3 (a), (b)). Any agitation during the washing process of the skin being cleaned will lead to exposure of more dirt surface to the detergent molecules remaining in the water and they will take up their positions as illustrated. Once this has happened, the dirt surface exposed can no longer attach itself to the skin. With further agitation the dirt particle will be broken loose and completely surrounded by detergent molecules.

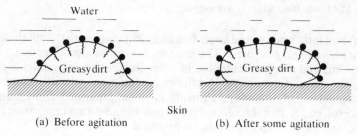

Water

Greasy dirt

Greasy dirt

Skin

(a) Before agitation (b) After some agitation

Fig. 12.3 Dirt removal action of a detergent

3. Emulsification of dirt

This is the final stage in the cleaning process and is illustrated in Fig. 12.4. Each dirt particle now has an outer layer of detergent molecules with their hydrophilic heads projecting into the wash water. Each head will carry the same type of electrical charge provided only one type of detergent is used, i.e. the heads will be all positive or all negative. As a result the dirt particles will have a surface layer of electric charge. Should they move in their random motion closer to each other, electrical repulsion between similar charges will keep them apart and the emulsion is maintained. The emulsified dirt will be lost in the water that escapes down the waste pipe of the wash-basin or shower tray.

Soap manufacture and action

Soap is made by the action of an alkali on animal and vegetable fats and oils. These latter are mixtures of triglycerides (see Ch. 11), so the reaction involves the break-up of the glycerol esters to liberate fatty acids which then form salts with the alkali thus:

1. Glycerol tristearate + water $\longrightarrow$ glycerol + stearic acid
2. Stearic acid + sodium hydroxide $\longrightarrow$ sodium stearate + water

Glycerol tristearate is used as an example of a triglyceride and so the soap produced would be sodium stearate. In practice, however, several

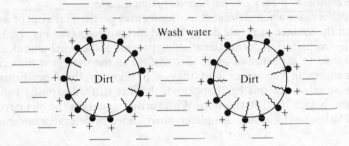

Fig. 12.4 Emulsifying action of a detergent

different fatty acids would be set free and form soaps with the alkali, and other alkalis may be used. The process, known as *saponification*, is a slow one and involves a number of other features not suggested in the simple description above. Addition of common salt will cause a precipitation of the soap, allowing it to be separated from water, glycerol, etc. A manufacturer of hard soap will also wish to separate the glycerol, which is an important by-product.

Whichever oils and alkalis are used in the process, the product will consist of mixtures of salts of a strong base and various fatty acids. Sodium stearate can serve as an example. In water it will ionise thus:

Sodium stearate ⟶ sodium ions (positive) + stearate ions (negative)

The stearate ions will carry the hydrophobic hydrocarbon chain from the fatty acid and will consequently act as the detergent molecules when soap is used to clean, or as the emulsifier molecules when soap is formed during the making of cleansing and day creams (see Ch. 6). Soaps are, therefore, anionic detergents and emulsifiers.

Experiment 12.1 Preparation of a soap sample

Before commencing this experiment, goggles should be put on and worn throughout. Place about 2 cm³ of castor oil in a glass beaker and add about 10 cm³ of 5 M sodium hydroxide solution. Warm the beaker and stir the contents carefully with a glass rod until they come to the boil. Continue boiling for a few minutes while stirring all the time.

Now add about 10 cm³ of distilled water and six spatula measures of common salt and boil gently for two to three minutes with stirring. Let the mixture cool, then stir to break up any large pieces of solid which have been formed and pass through a filter. Wash the solid on the filter with a little distilled water and allow to dry. Finally take a small quantity of the solid and shake with distilled water in a test tube. The formation of lather shows soap is present.

Disadvantages of soap

Experiment 7.2 demonstrated the four chief disadvantages of soap as a detergent. Taking sodium stearate soap as an example, an explanation of these can be offered thus:

1. Sodium stearate is the salt from the strong base, sodium hydroxide, and weak stearic acid. In Chapter 10 we saw that such a salt would give an alkaline reaction in water and this is why soap solutions have a pH around 9·0.
2. Added to hard water containing calcium or magnesium salts an insoluble scum is formed as in the reaction:

   Sodium stearate + calcium sulphate ⟶ calcium stearate (scum) + sodium sulphate (dissolved)

3. Soaps are only partially soluble in cold water and if common salt is added to the water, this greatly increases the concentration of sodium ions in the water. The equilibrium between dissolved and undissolved soap is thereby upset, and in order to reduce the sodium ion concentration more dissolved soap comes out of solution. This is what takes place if we try to use soap in sea water, but is made use of in the separation of soap during manufacture.
4. Since fatty acids are very weak acids, almost any other acid added to a soap solution will produce an insoluble fatty acid precipitate thus:

   Sodium stearate + citric acid ⟶ stearic acid (insoluble) + sodium citrate (dissolved)

   This fact would lead to problems in hairdressing if a soap-based shampoo were used to wash hair followed by a conditioner containing an organic acid. The insoluble fatty acid would stick to the hair and scalp.

Use of stearates in powders

Talcum powder and face powder always contain a small percentage of an ingredient to help the powder to stick to the skin. This is usually either magnesium stearate or zinc stearate. Magnesium stearate would be present in the scum formed by soap added to hard water containing magnesium salts, and its property of adherence is made use of in cosmetic powders. Zinc stearate is a very similar compound.

Soapless detergents

Most of the disadvantages of soaps stem from the fact that they are salts of fatty acids. Modern soapless detergents are manufactured to avoid this structure but the detergent molecule must still possess hydrophilic and hydrophobic parts. The hydrophobic part is derived from a vegetable or mineral oil which forms one of the raw materials used in manufacture. Sulphuric acid is generally used in the process to produce a detergent which is either a sulphate or a sulphonate.

Modern shampoos contain a detergent derived from *coconut oil*. Although this is a mixture of triglycerides, a large proportion of it is glycerol laurate, an ester of the fatty acid, lauric acid. During manufacture this is converted to the fatty alcohol, *lauryl alcohol*. By controlling conditions, only one of the two hydrogen atoms in sulphuric acid molecules is replaced by the lauryl group to make the compound, lauryl hydrogen sulphate. The remaining hydrogen atom can be allowed to react with any suitable base to produce the final detergent molecule. For example, if sodium hydroxide is used the detergent is called *sodium lauryl sulphate*.

This detergent ionises to give positive sodium ions and negative lauryl sulphate ions, and it is these latter ions that surround the dirt particles because they contain the hydrophobic remnant of the original coconut oil. It is, therefore, an anionic detergent just like soap but:

(a) it is a strong base/strong acid salt giving pH 7·0 in water;
(b) it does not form scum because calcium and magnesium lauryl sulphates are soluble;
(c) it is more soluble than soaps so salt in the water does not precipitate it;
(d) being a sulphate, it is unaffected by the presence of other acids.

An even more soluble lauryl sulphate can be made using the unusual base, triethanolamine, to manufacture the detergent *triethanolamine lauryl sulphate*. This, however, will not remedy the main disadvantage of all lauryl sulphates in shampoos which is due to their great efficacy as grease removers. Because of this they tend to leave hair in a dry, unmanageable state, so the lauryl sulphate molecule is modified to overcome this problem and shampoos now usually include a lauryl ether sulphate instead.

Questions

1. What is meant by the terms 'hydrophilic' and 'hydrophobic', and how are these properties built into an emulsifier molecule?
2. Explain what is meant by (a) an anionic detergent, (b) a cationic detergent and (c) a non-ionic detergent. How do these detergents keep dirt emulsified after washing the skin or hair?
3. State three disadvantages of soap and explain how a lauryl sulphate overcomes these.
4. What is (a) a wetting agent, (b) saponification and (c) triethanolamine?

Chapter 13

Coloured compounds

Colour is produced in cosmetics such as face powder, lipstick, blusher and eye make-up by blending in one or more compounds capable of absorbing some of the light wavelengths in the visible spectrum. The unabsorbed wavelengths are reflected or transmitted, and they give the colour we see. This chapter seeks to give some explanation of how this occurs and to indicate the type of compounds chosen.

Dyes, pigments and lakes

A dye is a coloured compound which is soluble in water, alcohol or oil, the chief solvents used in cosmetics. We can say *dyes* are *soluble colours*. If a coloured compound is not soluble in any of these solvents it is called a pigment, and so we can say *pigments* are *insoluble colours*. In general pigments are preferred in cosmetics because:

1. They will not spread in the sweat or sebum on the skin's surface,
2. They will not permanently colour the skin by dissolving in skin tissue fluid,
3. They will not streak due to rain or tears.

Unfortunately, the range of colours available as true pigment is quite restricted whereas there exists a vast range of dye colours. To be able to make use of the latter it is necessary to render a dye insoluble. This is done by absorbing the dye on the surface of a metal oxide or hydroxide which itself is insoluble but not coloured. The result is known as a *lake*, and lakes are used as alternatives to pigments in coloured cosmetics.

Inorganic pigments

Most pigments are not carbon compounds and are referred to as being inorganic. They are used extensively in eye make-up. They may also be used in nail enamel and as the non-staining colour in lipstick. They often prove to be *metallic oxides*, especially those of iron, manganese and chromium. Due to the presence of impurities a range of colours is possible with the same basic compound. The therapist should think of the various colours that iron rust may assume to appreciate how this range of pigment colour can be. Iron oxide can be obtained in black, brown, red and yellow forms, sometimes mixed with manganese oxide. Chromium oxide gives green and salts of chromium are often the basis of other colours. Inorganic pigments also include blue ultramarine (made by fusing together sodium, sulphur and other materials), black powdered carbon and powdered metals.

The mechanism of light absorption at certain wavelengths to produce colour can involve the electron arrangement within the metal atoms of the pigment. Certain metals always produce coloured compounds and are found among the transitional elements of the chemist's periodic table. This is a table which arranges all elements in order according to the number of protons in the atomic nucleus. Transitional elements are found grouped together in this table and are so called because the positioning of their electrons in shells makes a departure from what seems like a logical sequence in other elements. As stated above, however, the colour of a pigment may be due to other elements being present in small amounts, the colour depending on which element is the impurity.

Molecular structure of dyes

Dyes are usually organic compounds and many do not occur naturally, having been developed by chemical research. The synthetic dyes originate from unexpected sources, an important one being coal tar from which is derived the compound *aniline*, the starting compound for a large range of dyestuffs.

Many dye molecules have rings of atoms within their structure. One such ring is found to make up the molecule of the liquid called *benzene*. This ring is also found in a molecule of aniline. It is such a common feature of a great number of compound molecules that it is often represented by a 'shorthand' version in diagrams depicting molecular structure (see Fig. 13.1 (a), (b)). In the shorthand version it is assumed that there is a carbon atom at each corner of the hexagon with a single hydrogen atom attached. The circle is to indicate that the double bonds may exist in different positions between the carbon atoms.

Benzene is a colourless liquid so it does not absorb any particular band of visible wavelengths, but has been found to absorb certain invisible ultra-violet wavelengths. By removing some of the hydrogen atoms around the ring in a chemical reaction and substituting other groups of atoms in their place, the resulting compound may be able to absorb some visible wavelengths. This means the compound is coloured. A group of atoms that can cause such a change is said to be *chromophoric* and an example of such a group is the nitro group (see Fig. 13.2).

Addition of chromophoric groups to the benzene ring structure does not create a dye. The compound will be only weakly coloured and

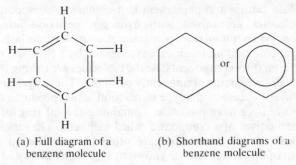

(a) Full diagram of a
benzene molecule

(b) Shorthand diagrams of a
benzene molecule

Fig. 13.1 Benzene ring structure

cannot attach itself to the object to be dyed. To complete the synthesis, certain other groups are made to replace hydrogen atoms around the ring. They bring out the colour and convey true dyeing properties to the molecule. These groups are called *auxchromes* and include the amino and hydroxyl arrangements of atoms. The therapist should note once again how polar properties become important in promoting attraction between different compounds.

Some important cosmetic dyes

The dyes whose molecular structure is illustrated in Fig. 13.2 are known as *nitro-dyes* because of the presence of the nitro group in their molecules. Since these molecules are small, they can penetrate the cuticle of the hair and are used as semi-permanent hair colourants. The most common dyes used in cosmetics are those derived from aniline and they are known as *azo-dyes* after a feature always found in their molecules and called an azo bridge. This bridge contains two nitrogen atoms which link together two benzene rings. This results in a larger and more complex molecule than a nitro-dye molecule. Azo dyes, in the form of lakes, are used in nail enamel, lipstick and blusher.

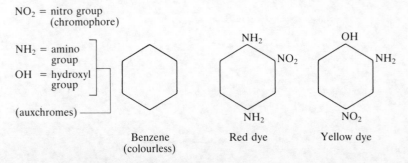

NO$_2$ = nitro group
(chromophore)

NH$_2$ = amino group

OH = hydroxyl group

(auxchromes)

Benzene
(colourless)

Red dye

Yellow dye

Fig. 13.2 Molecular structure of dyes

In eye-lash tinting and permanent hair-colouring, compounds with small molecules are mixed with hydrogen peroxide just before application. When this mixture penetrates the cuticle of the lash or head hairs, larger coloured molecules are synthesised by a chemical reaction between the mixture components. As the molecules are too big to escape from the hair, it remains permanently coloured. These dyes are called *oxidation dyes* because of the type of reaction which produces them.

Bromo-acid dyes have molecules containing several ring structures and are derivatives of a compound called xanthene. They include the well-known red dye, eosin, and are often used as the lip-staining component of lipstick. Some are known to act as sensitisers and so may be the culprit if a client reacts allergically to a particular colour.

As with most materials used in cosmetics, there is a comprehensive EEC directive governing the use by manufacturers in Europe of dyes and pigments with special restrictions applying to lipsticks and eye make-up. This is because the lips and the eyes are very sensitive areas of the human body and are easily inflamed by the presence of an unfamiliar compound. With lipstick there is also the problem of the colour entering the digestive system and being absorbed into the blood stream.

Questions

1. What differences exist between dyes and pigments? Explain what is meant by a lake in cosmetics and why they may be used in products.
2. What is meant by the terms (a) chromophore and (b) auxchrome in connection with dye chemistry? Give an example of each.
3. Write short notes on (a) inorganic pigments, (b) oxidation dyes and (c) EEC directive on colours.

Chapter 14

Perfumes

Whether used by themselves, or as additives to almost all cosmetics, there is no doubt that perfumes form one of the most important products of the industry. They will probably be the most costly ingredient in the cosmetic and reasons for this will emerge later. A perfume is defined as a blend of odorous materials from natural and synthetic sources which gives a pleasant overall odorous impression, and it will be the creation of a very skilled craftsman or craftswoman known as a *perfumier* or 'nose'.

Creation and composition of perfumes

A perfumier regards his or her skill as comparable to that of a composer of music. The perfumier's work-bench will include shelves housing bottles containing samples of all kinds of scent-producing materials. By selecting from these and mixing in various proportions, blends can be produced and improved upon until the nose of the 'nose' decides that a marketable product has been created. Because of the similarity with composing a piece of music, the work-bench where perfumes first originate is called an 'organ'.

The comparison with music does not end there. In the perfume blend will be ingredients of varying degrees of volatility. The most volatile are those which are the first to register a response in the *olfactory organ* of the purchaser's nose. These ingredients are called the *top-notes* of the perfume, but if they were used alone to make the blend, the impression created would be rather an insipid one. Less volatile components, known as *middle-notes*, are added to give what is called 'body' and character to the perfume.

When a therapist, or her client, purchases a sample of a commercial perfume she expects the odorous impression gained from the product to be the same on using the last few drops as was experienced on first opening the container. This would not be so if only top and middle-note ingredients were used. The more volatile top notes would evaporate in the early days and dominate the sensation detected by the nose, leaving the middle notes eventually to be the only source of smell. To control the rate of evaporation of material so as to produce a constant and persistent impression, ingredients of a third type are added and these are called the *base-notes* of the perfume.

The scent-producing materials to be found on the perfumier's work bench fall into three categories:

1. Products of plant origin including essential oils and gum extracts known as resinoids and balsams.
2. Products of animal origin.
3. Synthetically-produced compounds.

Essential oils

These oils obtained their name as a group in the early days of cosmetic technology. It was felt necessary to distinguish them from other vegetable oils which do not produce a pleasant-smelling vapour, or 'essence'. These latter were given the name of 'fixed oils' because they were non-volatile. A comparison of properties is given in Table 14.1.

Table 14.1   Properties of oils

Property	Essential oils	Fixed oils
Volatility	High	Low
Odorous impression	Pleasant	Little, or none
Soluble in alcohol	Yes	Castor oil only
Viscosity	Low	Medium

Essential oils are obtained from the flowers, fruits, leaves, etc. of many types of plants which are specially cultivated in a number of different parts of the world. The harvesting of the plants often takes place at unsocial hours and may involve hand-picking. Jasmine flowers, for example, grown in the fields around Grasse in southern France must be picked early in the day, or the essential oil will have evaporated in the mid-day sun. The high labour costs involved as a result help to make the final perfume expensive. Some important essential oils are:

1. Citronella oil – obtained from long grass grown in Java and other places.
2. Lemongrass – obtained from a grass grown in India, Africa and the West Indies.
3. Oil of lavender and oil of rosemary – obtained from the flowers and stalks and grown in France and Spain.
4. Citrus oils – obtained from oranges, lemons and limes.

It is interesting to note that different parts of the same tree can produce different oils. From an orange tree, for example, we get orange oil from its fruit, neroli from its flowers and pettigrain from its leaves.

The quantity of essential oil extracted from a given weight of plant material is usually quite small, a tonne of flowers perhaps yielding only a kilogram of oil, and this proves a further factor in making perfumes expensive. Three methods are used and these are discussed next.

1. Expression

This is the method used to obtain citrus oils. The peel of the picked fruit is placed between the jaws of a press which are then forced closer together, causing the oil to exude out of the peel. Bergamot and pettigrain are among the oils produced in this way.

2. Steam or vacuum distillation

Any process which attempted to boil off an essential oil under normal atmospheric conditions would result in chemical decomposition of the oil by the high temperature involved. Two methods are used to lower the temperature required. In the first of these, steam is passed into the plant material which causes a mixture of water vapour and oil vapour to distill off at a temperature much lower than the boiling point of the oil. The distillate is then led off to a cooler part of the apparatus where both vapours condense into a receiver. Being non-miscible, the oil and water form separate layers, allowing the water to be run off, so leaving the oil behind (see Fig. 14.1).

Instead of using steam, in the second method the distillation plant is sealed from the atmosphere and connected to a vacuum pump working on the same principle as the vacuum suction machine in the salon. This lowers the inside pressure and hence the boiling point of the essential oil, which can now be driven off at a safe temperature from the original plant material.

3. Solvent extraction

This process makes use of the ability of a liquid or semi-solid to take the essential oil into solution. A very simple application of this method is often employed on a small scale as a cottage industry in some parts of the

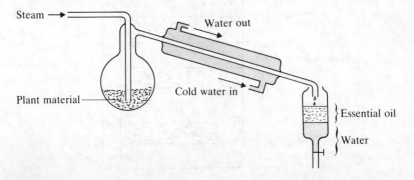

Fig. 14.1 Steam distillation of an essential oil

world. It is then called *enfleurage*. Alternate layers of fat and plant material are built up in a suitable vat (see Fig. 14.2), and then left in contact with each other for a number of days or even weeks. Essential oil gradually diffuses into the fat which acts as a solvent and produces a pomade of pleasant-smelling fat. The pomade is often used in this form, for example, as a hairdressing oil, although further separation could take place.

On a larger, and more technical, scale the plant material is subjected to continuous washing by a very volatile solvent, which takes the essential oil into solution, together with waxes and pigments. This solution can then be filtered off from the plant debris and the oil separated from solvent by some form of fractional distillation. The resulting product is called an *absolute*, e.g. if obtained from jasmine flowers it would be jasmine absolute.

Animal scent-producing products

Other ingredients represented on the perfumier's organ and which, by themselves, do not have an attractive odour are certain secretions and extractions from special animals. They are included in perfumes to give them the mysterious property of 'body', or, in other words, to help provide middle-notes and base-notes. Four products come under this heading and they are:

1. Musk – obtained from a Tibetan musk deer and expensive.
2. Ambergris – produced in the intestine of a sperm whale and found floating on the sea. It is also expensive.
3. Civet – from the African civet cat.
4. Castor – a secretion obtained from a beaver, and not to be confused with castor oil.

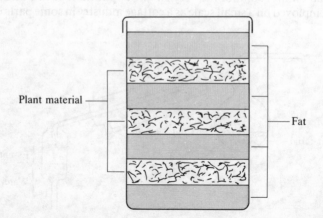

Plant material

Fat

Fig. 14.2 Extraction of essential oils by enfleurage

Synthetic ingredients

The modern chemical industry has also come to the aid of the perfumier, and it is quite common nowadays for even an expensive perfume to contain synthetic ingredients. These may be either factory-made copies of compounds found in essential oils and known as *isolates*, or entirely new odorous substances not so far found to occur naturally, but nevertheless acceptable to the experienced 'nose'.

Compatibility with the product

Many fragrances created by the perfumier will be included in cosmetics as a small percentage additive. Consequently it will need to be unchanged chemically by the other major ingredients of the product. In perfumed soap, for example, the perfume must exist in the presence of the mildly alkaline fatty-acid salts of sodium or potassium. The designing of a perfume must take such uses into account. Sometimes the active ingredient is too potent as a reactive chemical to allow the inclusion of any perfume in the product, desirable as that might be. This is the problem with chemical depilatories (see Ch. 18) and permanent-waving solutions where the active ingredient has a somewhat objectionable smell and cannot be masked.

Questions

1. What is meant by the terms (a) top-notes, (b) middle-notes and (c) base-notes as applied to perfume?
2. Toilet water is a diluted form of perfume. Which liquid would you expect to be used for diluting, and why?
3. The essential oil from lavender flowers is obtained by steam distillation, but the oil from bergamot fruit is obtained by expression. Compare these processes.
4. What is (a) ambergris, (b) rose absolute, (c) a compatible perfume?

Chapter 15

Preservatives

In this final chapter of our consideration of cosmetic ingredients we arrive at a group of compounds whose presence in a cosmetic is not essential for it to perform effectively. Therapists and their clients might question the need for adding preservatives on the grounds that they take away the naturalness of a given product, so let us consider the case in their favour.

Functions of preservatives

Preservatives are added to cosmetics for two purposes:

1. They control the number and type of micro-organisms present in the product so that the health of the person using it is not adversely affected.
2. They prevent the product from deteriorating both during its shelf life and when in use.

Sources of contamination

Micro-organisms may enter the cosmetic via the raw materials chosen to manufacture it. A good example of this happening can be seen in talc, which is used for its property of imparting slip to a powder (see Ch. 7). It is obtained from the ground by mining in Italy, France and India, and as a result it can often carry spores of the bacterium causing tetanus. In this state at ground temperature the spores are harmless as they do not multiply, but if such talc is included in a powder which is then applied to the skin, the spores find conditions more congenial and start to multiply as vegetative cells. To prevent this happening, all talc used in cosmetics must be sterilised before use.

Contamination may also occur during production of the cosmetic, when sources could include the vats, tanks, pipes, etc. of the industrial plant, the washing or cooling water and even the hands and clothing of operatives. Once purchased and put into use, the danger is still not over, for the user's skin may be carrying pathogenic organisms and these can easily transfer to the container where they might begin to multiply.

Experiment 15.1   Contamination of skin by bacteria
Obtain two petri-dishes with lids and containing nutrient agar jelly.
Sterilise by putting them in an oven at 100°C for fifteen minutes.
Remove carefully, making sure the lids cover the jelly, and allow them to
cool. Now raise the lid of one dish just enough to enable you to touch the
surface of the jelly with unwashed fingertips. Replace the lid quickly and
incubate at 40°C. After washing the hands, repeat the process with the
other dish. Examine each dish *without raising the lid* at intervals during
the following week and notice if a colony of bacteria has developed on
the jelly surface. When the experiment is over make sure the dishes and
lids are sterilised again.

Micro-organisms and the cosmetic

Whether contamination of the cosmetic is likely to give problems or not
will be determined by how suitable a habitat it proves to be for the
organism. The life processes must be able to continue sufficiently freely
to enable cell division to take place so that a colony develops within the
cosmetic. The chemical changes brought about by the colony as a result
of its metabolism will then cause the health and deterioration hazards
already referred to.

Most micro-organisms require the presence of *water* to survive so we
could expect to find them in products that are simple aqueous solutions
such as shampoos. The water phase of an emulsion would also prove an
attractive habitat, particularly when the water forms the continuous
phase. Lotions which are oil/wax mixtures and products like nail
varnish based on solvents other than water are less likely to support
microbial activity.

There must also be present in the product a compound which can be
used as a *nutrient* by the contaminating organism. Powders containing
starch to give bloom (see Ch. 7) and products containing proteins for
thickening and gelling are obvious examples of this, but some micro-
organisms have been found to be able to break down quite unexpected
compounds, such as detergents and emulsifiers, to derive energy.

The *pH value* of the product will also be a factor in encouraging or
discouraging multiplication. Most organisms can tolerate a habitat if
the pH lies between 5·0 and 8·0, and some moulds have been found to
survive even lower values. We should expect, therefore, cosmetics like
antiperspirants, chemical depilatories and cuticle remover not to require
the addition of preservatives as their pH values lie outside this range.

Most micro-organisms that give problems if allowed to colonise a
cosmetic are found to be aerobic. This means they require a supply of
oxygen to survive. They will find the interface between the cosmetic and
the atmosphere most congenial, although, since oxygen has a certain
solubility in water, products containing this will again suggest the use of
preservatives. On the other hand, anaerobic bacteria if present would

find the presence of an antioxidant positively helpful, as it would keep the oxygen level quite low.

Factors affecting the choice of a preservative

The factors to be considered in making a choice of preservative will be:

(a) the nature of the organism likely to be the contaminant, if known;
(b) the possibility of side-effects on the skin, or other parts of the body;
(c) the possible changes that might occur to the cosmetic as a result of adding a preservative.

The changes envisaged under (c) could involve a deterioration in colour, smell or physical state. A particular example of this is the 'ropey' appearance of certain emulsified products which can occur due to protein breakdown by the preservative.

Typical preservatives

A list of preservatives used in cosmetics would include:

1. Chlorinated derivatives of phenol.
2. Benzoic acid and its derivatives.
3. Parahydroxy-benzoic acid and its esters, known in the industry as 'parabens'.
4. Cationic detergents.
5. Essential oils.
6. Formaldehyde.

Antioxidants

Reference has already been made to the problems associated with oxidation of unsaturated oils in Chapter 11. Antioxidants are a class of preservative used to combat these and they also compete with aerobic micro-organisms for the available atmospheric oxygen. Ascorbic acid, lecithin and certain sulphites are often used for this purpose.

Questions

1. Why may the existence of micro-organisms in a cosmetic product present a hazard?
2. Select one type of cosmetic where conditions in it may encourage bacterial growth, and one type where the reverse will apply, and explain why in each case.
3. What adverse effect might a preservative have if added to an emulsified cream?

Part 4
Salon treatments

Chapter 16

Electric currents in the salon

In Chapter 4 we saw that an electric current may be either a flow of electrons or a flow of ions. In parts of circuits which consist of metal wires, electrons flow, but in aqueous solutions of electrolytes the flow is ionic. In this chapter we shall be largely concerned with the uses of electric currents when flowing through the tissues of a client's body. Here we have the current being conducted by aqueous solutions of salts so it will be an ion current. Both types of current may be either direct currents (D.C.) or alternating currents (A.C.).

Graphical representation of a current

In order to understand the differences between the various currents used in the salon, it is necessary to show how they can be represented on a graph of current intensity against time. In Fig. 16.1 two types of D.C. current are plotted. In steady D.C. (Fig. 16.1a), after the initial switch-on period, the current intensity remains constant at a certain value, but in fluctuating D.C. (Fig. 16.1b) the intensity rises from zero to a maximum value and then falls to zero again, repeating the changes as time progresses.

To represent an alternating current on a graph, we have to have a means of showing intensity changes when the current direction reverses.

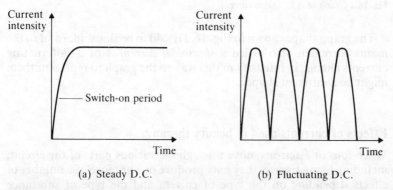

(a) Steady D.C.   (b) Fluctuating D.C.

Fig. 16.1 Graphs of steady and fluctuating D.C.

This is done by drawing the graph of the reversed current below the time axis, in the same way that negative values of *y* are plotted on a graph in mathematics. Figure 16.2 shows this being done for the intensity changes which occur when a simple appliance such as a radiant heat lamp is connected to the A.C. mains. Notice how the intensity rises and falls in a similar way to the fluctuating D.C. but then, when the current direction reverses, the graph is repeated but inverted. When the intensity has assumed all its different values, we say a cycle is completed and from then onwards the graph repeats itself. In the UK mains supply a cycle is over in one fiftieth of a second but in the USA it takes one sixtieth of a second. The number of cycles completed in one second is called the *frequency* of the alternating current. Frequency used to be expressed in cycles per second, but the unit used now is the *hertz (Hz)*. Thus the mains frequency in the UK is 50 Hz and in USA it is 60 Hz.

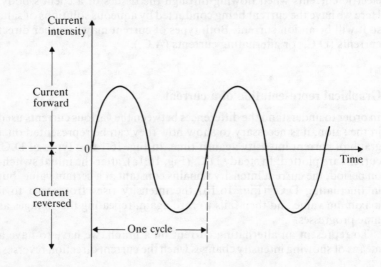

Fig. 16.2 Graph of A.C. mains current

The graph shape shown in Fig. 16.2 is said to be sinusoidal and so the mains current is also called a *sinusoidal current*. Not all alternating currents change in intensity in this way so the graph to represent them might be a different shape.

Effects of currents used in beauty therapy

When ions or electrons move through the various parts of the circuit, including living tissues, they may produce one or more of a number of effects depending on the type of current and the type of substance through which they flow. These include:

1. Heat production (see Ch. 4).
2. Chemical changes.
3. Muscle or nerve stimulation.
4. Magnetic fields (see Ch. 17).

Any type of current is capable of producing heating and magnetic effects. Only direct currents produce chemical effects, and slowly-changing intensity currents are required for stimulatory effects.

Currents in electrolytes

Reference has already been made in Chapter 4 to the presence of two types of ion when an electrolyte is in aqueous solution. These were called cations (positive charge) and anions (negative charge) and got their names from the electrode to which they are attracted when the solution becomes part of a circuit (see Fig. 16.3). Thus when an electric current flows in an electrolyte solution, such as human tissue, there is a two-way movement of ions.

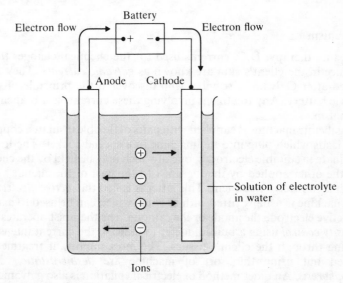

Fig. 16.3 Movement of ions in an electrolyte

When the cations arrive at the cathode they meet electrons which have been driven there away from the negative terminal of the battery, or other source of electrical pressure. Electrical neutralisation takes place thus:

Cation (positive) + electron(s) (negative) ⟶ uncharged particle

Anions, on the other hand, arrive at the anode, give up one or more of the electrons from the atoms which compose them, and also become neutral thus:

Anion (negative) – electron(s) (negative) ———▶ uncharged particle

The released electrons at the anode then move through the connecting wires attracted by the positive terminal of the battery.

The uncharged particles produced when ions are neutralised are often very chemically active and are responsible for the chemical effect of an electric current. A chemical reaction always involves the production of a new substance. When a direct current flows through an electrolyte solution, these substances appear at the electrodes only and may take the form of deposits on the electrodes, bubbles of gas or changes in the composition of the solution near the electrode. It is this latter that is made great use of in the beauty salon.

Using the explanation above, the therapist should consider why these chemical effects are not observed with even low frequency A.C. such as that supplied by the mains.

Galvanism

In beauty therapy, D.C. currents used for the chemical changes they produce in the client's skin are known as *galvanic currents*. They are named after Galvani, a scientist who discovered the principle of the electric battery. Any treatment involving these currents is a branch of galvanism.

A galvanic machine is supplied with pairs of flexible insulated copper wire leads which plug into the machine in a special socket. The leads terminate in suitable electrodes, one of which may be held by the client and the other applied by the therapist to the part of the client's skin which is to receive treatment. This latter is called the *active electrode*. The machine is usually fitted with a switch which can be used to make the active electrode the anode or the cathode. The therapist operates an *intensity control* using a built-in meter to indicate the current intensity passing through the client's tissues. The most important treatments carried out using this sort of machine are *desincrustation* and *iontophoresis*. An older method of electrical epilation is also galvanic in character and is discussed in Chapter 18.

Experiment 16.1   Alkali production at the cathode
Take a strip of red litmus paper and wet it completely with tap water. Place the wet strip on the surface of a ceramic tile or other suitable insulating surface. Connect leads to the terminals of a 6 volt battery or powerpack and terminate these with 4 mm plugs, or other suitable electrode material. Making sure that the plugs do not make direct

contact with each other, hold them in contact with the litmus paper at a distance of 2 to 3 cm apart. After a few minutes with current flowing through the wet paper, remove the plugs and note that a blue spot has formed under the plug connected to the negative terminal of the battery. This indicates the formation of alkali.

For the type of salts which occur in the water of the human skin, the result of the chemical effect of electricity is to produce an excess of hydroxyl ions under the cathode during galvanic treatment (see Expt 16.1). This can be explained by considering what happens in a sodium chloride solution in water. There will be present sodium ions (positive) and chloride ions (negative) from the salt. In addition, as in any water sample, a small proportion of the water molecules will be ionised to give equal numbers of hydrogen ions (positive) and hydroxyl ions (negative). When a current flows through the solution, sodium ions and hydrogen ions will be attracted to the cathode, but for reasons not explained here it will be the hydrogen ions which will be discharged as they receive electrons from the cathode. They will become atoms of hydrogen and so form the hydrogen gas bubbles evolved at the cathode. In this way the solution around the cathode loses hydrogen ions first upsetting the balance between hydrogen and hydroxyl ions and so gives rise to the hydroxyl ion excess in that part of the solution. This alkaline effect is made use of in desincrustation. The active electrode is made the cathode and is moved about over the client's skin. The alkali produced under it destroys flakes of keratin, since keratin is a protein. Often the active electrode takes the form of a roller which only contacts the skin in a small area and so concentrates the produced alkali to achieve a successful result.

The therapist should be aware that, although this chemical effect can be put to good use as described above, it can also result in a *galvanic burn* if conditions are incorrect. If the area of contact between skin and cathode is too small and the current intensity high, an excessive concentration of alkali will be produced which may result in destruction of skin protein to deeper levels within the epidermis, and perhaps the dermis. Galvanic burns may also result from allowing the current to flow for too long a time.

Iontophoresis is a treatment which seeks to inject beneficial ions, or remove harmful ions from the skin (see Fig. 16.4). Suppose, for example, that it was considered desirable to drive amino-acids into the skin. A solution in water of the acid could be made up and used to soak a pad of cotton wool which was then placed under the cathode of a galvanic machine. The solution would contain positive hydrogen ions and negative amino-acid ions. If the anode also made contact with the client, ions would move between the electrodes, and in the soaked pad amino-acid ions would be repelled by the cathode causing them to move into the skin.

In the salon commercially made-up products are often used for this treatment. Here the manufacturer's instructions state under which

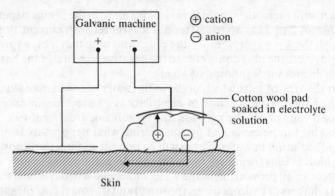

Fig. 16.4 Principle of iontophoresis

electrode the product should be employed. At present manufacturers in the UK are not obliged by law to disclose the nature of the ingredients present but the therapist can deduce from Fig. 16.4 that the ion being driven into the skin carries the same type of electric charge as the polarity of the electrode under which the product is placed.

Faradic treatments

In the salon faradic machines are used to stimulate muscles so that they contract and relax in an involuntary way. This muscular movement uses energy which was stored as fat in the body and, as a result, the client loses weight. Faradic treatments can thus be an aid to slimming. They can also be used to bring muscles back into action after a long period of enforced rest.

Pairs of pads are attached to the client across appropriate parts of the anatomy and a suitable current passed between each pair using the body tissues as part of the circuit. By correct arrangement of the pads, the current will cross a motor nerve attached to a muscle, or the muscle directly. To promote successful contractions the current must be one whose intensity is increasing or decreasing but these changes must not occur too rapidly or the muscle will be unable to respond.

One of the first type of currents ever used to produce muscle contractions was a sinusoidal one obtained from the mains via a voltage-dropping transformer, and the therapist should use Fig. 16.2 to convince herself that such a current is continually changing in intensity as required. The frequency of the mains also proved to be low enough to give the slow changes needed. Unfortunately, a sinusoidal supply connected to a pair of pads also stimulated the sensory nerves sufficiently to cause a certain amount of pain for the client.

To overcome the disadvantage of a sinusoidal current, a special coil was designed for inclusion in the machine. Using the principles discovered by Michael Faraday, the coil produced a different type of alternating current whose intensity-time graph is shown in Fig. 16.5. The sharp peak in the forward direction provided the stimulation while the period of steady reverse current had no muscular effect. Because the coil produced alternating current, no chemical reaction occurred at the electrodes. The coil was known as a *faradic coil* and it gave its name to the muscle and nerve stimulating treatments for which it was used.

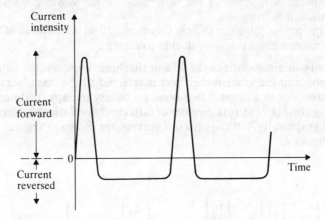

Fig. 16.5 Current from a faradic coil

Faradic machines used nowadays in the salon generate their special current by including electronic circuits. A graph of a modern faradic current is shown in Fig. 16.6. Although there is no reverse current, the time for which each forward pulse occurs is short enough for chemical effects to be negligible. The current can be described as an interrupted fluctuating direct current.

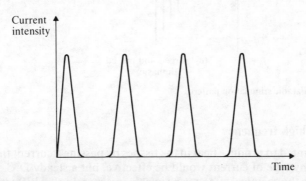

Fig. 16.6 Current from a modern faradic machine

A number of different controls will be found on a machine including:

1. Intensity control for each pair of pads. Meters are not usually fitted and the client's comfort is used to decide on the setting.
2. Frequency control of stimulating peaks. The frequency must be such that the muscle contraction is tetanic in character.
3. Contraction pulse length control. This will determine both the time for which the muscle is contracted and also the rest period.
4. Surge control. An automatic increase and/or decrease in intensity of peaks will assist in the dispersion of the waste products of muscular activity.
5. Monophasic/diphasic switch. Clients may find one or other of these variations more tolerable during treatment.

Detailed guidance on the use of faradic machines is outside the scope of this book and the student therapist is referred to the manufacturer's instructions or to a suitable text-book on beauty therapy treatments.

In Fig. 16.7 (a), (b), (c) a number of different stimulating patterns are shown graphically, but the peaks of current are shown as vertical lines for simplicity.

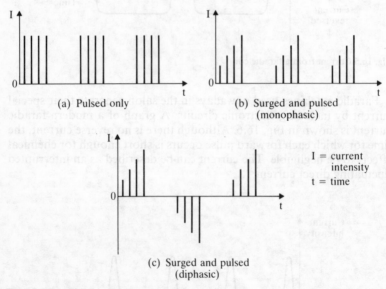

(a) Pulsed only

(b) Surged and pulsed (monophasic)

(c) Surged and pulsed (diphasic)

I = current intensity
t = time

Fig. 16.7 Faradic stimulation patterns

Use of high frequency

If we wanted to produce heat in the tissues by passing a current through them, any type of current would be effective, but a steady D.C. would also give the chemical effects used in galvanism and a slowly fluctuating

D.C. or low frequency A.C. would give the stimulatory effect of faradism in addition to heat. To avoid these extra effects in the salon and produce heat alone we turn to a *high frequency* alternating current. Opinions differ in the profession about the range of frequencies which should be included in this band, but values above 100 000 Hz would usually be accepted. Most high frequency equipment generates currents with frequencies well above this value. The current can be sinusoidal as it changes too rapidly to affect sensory nerves, one cycle being completed in less than ten millionths of a second.

High frequency currents have a number of unusual properties. They tend to travel in the surface of a conductor, which in beauty therapy will be advantageous as they will use the client's skin rather than deeper tissues. They also appear to pass through insulating material using the capacitor effect.

A *capacitor*, basically, consists of two conducting electrodes separated by a layer of an insulating substance. If one electrode is connected to a source of current and this results in its acquiring an excess of electrons, repulsive forces will be exerted on the electrons in the atoms of the other electrode. As a result, electrons will flow away from the surface of this second electrode leaving it positively charged. If the current source is alternating, electrons will move to the first electrode during one half of the cycle and away again during the second half. This means that the first electrode alternates between being negatively-charged and positively-charged in step with the alternating supply. The electrons in the second electrode will respond to these fluctuations and thus an alternating current of electrons will flow away from it and then back again at the same frequency. The higher the frequency of the current source, the more effective is this apparent transfer of current across the insulating substance. This is the reason why high frequency currents can be applied to the client's skin in the salon using 'electrodes' made of glass, or other non-conducting substance. The client's skin becomes the second electrode of a capacitor.

Diathermy is the term used to describe high frequency tissue heating. It is often referred to as short-wave diathermy. This is because we can imagine a high frequency current being like a wave passing through the tissues, and high frequency waves have short wavelengths (see Ch. 19). Even the sinusoidal graph (Fig. 16.2) looks wave-shaped.

Interferential currents

If two high frequency currents of slightly different frequencies are caused to flow through the same piece of tissue, they will interfere with each other in such a way that the tissue involved receives treatment as if it were being subjected to an alternating current whose frequency was just the difference between the two original currents. Such interference occurs when other kinds of fluctuations of slightly different frequency meet also (see Expt 16.2).

In beauty therapy interferential currents can be used to produce muscle stimulation in a restricted area of the body. Suppose electrodes A and B in Fig. 16.8 are connected to a circuit which generates a high frequency current of 1 000 050 Hz, and electrodes C and D to a circuit generating 1 000 000 Hz. When the machine head is placed on the client, a non-stimulating current flows through the tissues between A and B, and another between C and D. At P in the tissues, however, both currents interfere, and the effect produced is that of a 50 Hz current. This is a low enough frequency to produce a faradic effect in the region of P only.

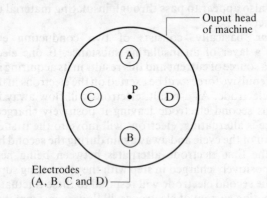

Fig. 16.8 Use of interferential currents

Experiment 16.2 Interference of sound waves
Take two tuning forks of the same frequency and attach a small piece of putty or other adhesive material to one of the tynes of one of the forks. This will cause it to vibrate at a slightly lower frequency. If both forks are now made to vibrate at the same time, a regular rise and fall in the sound intensity will be heard. The rise and fall frequency will be the same as the differences between the two fork frequencies. This is due to interference between the two sets of sound waves, and is analogous to the manner in which two interferential currents can be made to produce the effects of a lower frequency current.

Questions

1. With reference to the mains supply, explain the meanings of the terms (a) cycle, (b) frequency and (c) sinusoidal.
2. What is galvanism? Describe one form of galvanic treatment used in the beauty salon. Why must the galvanic machine produce steady D.C.?

3. With the aid of diagrams, explain what is meant in faradism by the terms (a) pulsed, (b) surged and (c) diphasic.
4. Why are high frequency currents used for tissue heating?
5. How could you determine, using simple apparatus, if the polarity switch of a galvanic machine were correctly connected and labelled?

Chapter 17

Salon machine circuits

In this chapter we investigate the components which help to make up the circuitry of the electrical machines used in salon treatment. A knowledge of how they operate will act as a background of information for the inquisitive therapist and take away some of the mystery surrounding the equipment available for purchase.

The electromagnet

A magnet is a familiar object to everyone. It is a device with the following properties:

1. It is able to attract certain metals, notably iron and steel.
2. Its power of attraction seems to be concentrated at places near its ends and they are called *poles*.
3. Freely suspended it will take up such a position that one pole appears to seek out the north pole and the other the south pole of the Earth and the magnet poles are named accordingly.
4. If two magnets are brought together, like poles repel and unlike poles attract each other.

In order to explain the ability of a magnet to attract objects with which it is not in contact, scientists say that the magnet is surrounded by a *magnetic field*.

When any current, D.C. or A.C., flows through a wire, the space surrounding the wire becomes a magnetic field. The easiest way to demonstrate this is to wind the wire in the form of a coil, or solenoid (see Expt 17.1 and Fig. 17.1).

Experiment 17.1 Demonstration of magnetic effect
Connect a coil of insulated copper wire wound with several hundred turns via a switch to a battery or other source of steady D.C. Include in your circuit a current-controlling resistor if necessary. Place a plotting compass, or a mounted compass needle, so that the axis of the coil is in a horizontal plane and passes through the centre of the needle but is at right angles to the north–south meridian line (the compass will point in this direction if the current is not flowing). Now switch on and note the

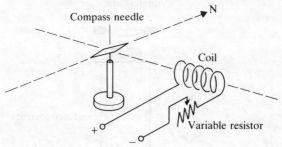

Fig. 17.1 Magnetic effect of electricity

movement of the needle towards the coil. Note also which end of the needle is closest to the coil.

Switch off the current and allow the needle to take up its north–south position. Reverse the connections to the coil and switch on again. The opposite end of the needle should now be attracted to the coil.

A coil of wire carrying a steady D.C. behaves as if one end is a north pole and the other end is a south pole. Reversing the current direction reverses polarity. If the core of the coil is filled with magnetic material a more powerful magnet results and if this material loses its magnetised state when the current is switched off, we have a very useful magnet which can be switched on and off when required. Such an arrangement is called an *electromagnet* (see Fig. 17.2). Soft iron is often chosen as the material for its core.

If an electromagnet is supplied with a low frequency A.C. its poles will keep continually reversing in step with current-direction reversals around the coil. This gives us the basis for a simple *vibrator* (see Fig. 17.3). A thin flexible disc of magnetic material, known as an armature, is held in a ring close to one pole of the electromagnet. Whenever the pole

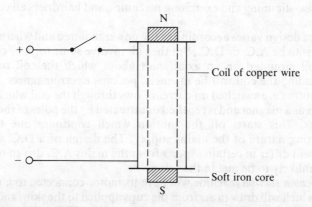

Fig. 17.2 The electromagnet

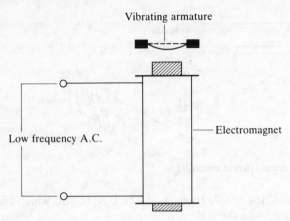

Fig. 17.3 Simple vibrator

is magnetised due to flow of current in the coil, the armature will be attracted towards the pole. The current will fall to zero before it reverses (see Fig. 16.2) and this means that the pole will cease to be magnetised. The flexible armature will return to its rest position but will be attracted again as the current flows in the opposite direction. A little thought will show that the armature will vibrate with twice the frequency of the A.C. supply.

Motors

The magnetic effect of an electric current is the basis for all applications of electricity involving movement. The electric motor is the most used method employed in equipment to obtain movement. Powerful vibrators, particularly those with flexible drives, vacuum suction machines, slimming and exercising machines, and hairdriers all contain a motor.

Motor design varies according to the power required and whether the supply is to be A.C. or D.C., but they all involve some form of copper wire coil mounted on an axial shaft about which the coil rotates. Surrounding the coil will be magnets, perhaps electromagnets. When most motors are switched on current flows through the coil which then behaves as a magnet and is repelled or attracted by the poles of the fixed magnets. This starts off the motion which continues due to the alternating nature of the mains supply. The design of a D.C. driven motor will differ in certain aspects from the mains A.C. driven motor, but is unlikely to be met in the salon.

A *vacuum suction* machine will have its motor connected to a rotary pump which will draw in air from the cups applied to the skin, and push it through an outlet into the salon atmosphere. This will cause skin tissues under the cup to bulge into the cup space in an attempt to replace the air that the pump has removed.

Electromagnetic induction

If the interaction between a magnet and wires carrying an electric current, as employed in a motor, can result in motion then we might expect that a combination of magnet and motion would result in a current being generated in a nearby wire. This was found to be so in a famous experiment conducted by Faraday, and the effect was called electromagnetic induction.

Experiment 17.2 Demonstration of electromagnetic induction

Set up the apparatus shown in Fig. 17.4, and move the magnet in and out of the coil along its axis. Note that a stationary magnet produces no reading on the meter but that a current is induced in the coil wires if the magnet moves. Reversing the polarity or direction of motion causes a reversal in the current direction.

The permanent magnet in Experiment 17.2 could be replaced by an electromagnet and the same effects would be observed. This phenomenon is the basis on which a power station generator works. There an electromagnet is rotated at high speed by being coupled to a steam or water turbine. A number of stationary coils mounted near the magnet have a current induced in them as a result, and this is used to supply electricity to the grid system.

The transformer

Another way of explaining the generation of an induced current as observed in Experiment 17.2 is to say that when the magnet is some

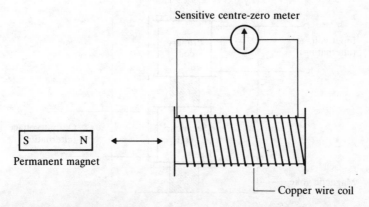

Fig. 17.4 Electromagnetic induction

distance from the coil the magnetic field strength due to it is quite weak in the vicinity of the coil, but as the magnet approaches the field strength increases. Similarly, when the magnet is drawn away from the coil this field strength decreases. During either of these changes a current is induced in the coil. We can say, therefore, that a *change* of magnetic field strength will result in an induced current in a wire, or other conductor.

This principle is made use of in the important electrical circuit component known as a *transformer*. A simple transformer consists of two copper wire coils sharing the same magnetic core, or yoke as it is called. One coil, known as the *primary coil*, should be thought of as behaving like an electromagnet. The other, known as the *secondary coil*, has currents induced in it due to magnetic field strength changes caused by the primary coil currents. A possible arrangement is shown in Fig. 17.5.

It is important to understand how these field strength changes are created. Instead of moving a magnet about, the primary coil is connected to an alternating voltage and so an alternating current flows in this coil and causes fluctuations and reversals of the state of magnetisation of the yoke, as described for a simple vibrator. Being wound round the yoke, the secondary coil will have alternating currents induced in it provided its terminals are connected to a complete circuit. In the absence of this circuit an alternating voltage will appear across its terminals as shown in Fig. 17.5.

It is found that a transformer works more efficiently if the yoke does not have ends, but continues as a complete ring, or rings, of magnetic material as indicated by the broken lines in Fig. 17.5. Notice also that transformers operate with an alternating input and that their output voltage is also alternating.

In beauty therapy machines:

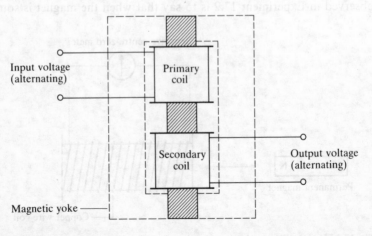

Fig. 17.5 The transformer

(a) transformers are used to change the mains voltage to a lower or higher value;

(b) transformers are used to isolate the client from the mains.

Their voltage-changing function is usually employed to reduce the electrical pressure to a safe value in the circuits of which the client may form a part (galvanic and faradic machines). The transformer can easily be designed to do this because:

$$\frac{\text{Output voltage}}{\text{Input voltage}} = \frac{\text{Secondary turns}}{\text{Primary turns}}$$

Example: Suppose we wish to reduce the voltage from 240 V to 40 V.

$$\frac{\text{Output voltage}}{\text{Input voltage}} = \frac{40}{240} = 1/6$$

Thus the number of turns on the secondary coil must be 1/6 of those on the primary coil. The latter could be wound with 600 turns which would mean that the secondary coil would need to have 100 turns.

Since the secondary coil in a normal transformer is not connected electrically to the primary coil, a machine which includes a transformer between the mains leads and the client's pads will have, thereby, an additional safety device since there is no risk of the client being connected to the live lead of the mains.

Rectifiers

Transformers cannot change A.C. to D.C. A device which does this is called a *rectifier*. Modern rectifiers used in salon machine circuits are usually made from substances called semiconductors but an explanation of how they operate is beyond the scope of this book. In electronics they are also called *diodes*.

We have already seen in Chapter 16 how a steady D.C. supply is required for galvanic treatments. This could be obtained from batteries, but it is more convenient to connect the machine to an A.C. mains socket in the salon and let the machine rectifier change A.C. to D.C. for us. In addition, the circuits which generate the special currents used in faradism need a D.C. supply as their source of energy, so again the manufacturer includes rectifiers inside the machine.

Rectifiers can be compared with the valves in veins or in the heart, these latter only allowing blood to flow in one direction. Rectifiers only allow current to flow in one direction.

Experiment 17.3   Rectifying action of a diode
Connect up the circuit shown in Fig. 17.6 taking care to choose a battery
to match the lamp working voltage. If the lamp lights on completing the

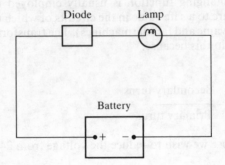

Fig. 17.6 Diode operation

circuit, disconnect the diode and reconnect it the other way round. You
will now note that the lamp remains unlit. Replace the battery with an
alternating voltage of the same value using a power pack or transformer
and repeat the experiment. Although the lamp remains lit throughout, a
cathode ray oscilloscope connected across it will give a trace on its
screen as shown in Fig. 17.7.

The trace obtained in Experiment 17.3 indicates that only half of each
cycle of the sinusoidal A.C. supply from the transformer is being
allowed through the lamp. A circuit can be arranged within the machine
which uses four rectifiers and will convert sinusoidal A.C. into a current
as represented graphically in Fig. 17.8. Most galvanic and faradic
machines contain this circuit.

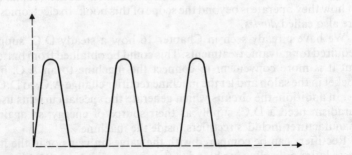

Fig. 17.7 Half-wave rectified current

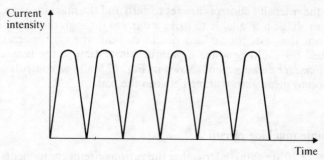

Fig. 17.8 Full-wave rectified current

Smoothing capacitor

The therapist will appreciate that the full-wave rectified current represented in Fig. 17.8 will be unsuitable for galvanic treatments as it changes in intensity and would be stimulatory. To convert such a supply to steady D.C. requires the use of another circuit component known as a *smoothing capacitor*. It is able to smooth out the fluctuations from the rectifier circuit because it has a capacity for storing electric charge.

Potentiometer as intensity controller

We have already referred in Chapter 16 to the intensity controls on galvanic and faradic machines. They have the outward appearance of a knob which rotates or a slider. Behind them inside the machine will be found a small coil of resistance wire which is connected across the supply voltage coming from the earlier parts of the circuit, as shown in Fig. 17.9. When the knob is rotated, or the slider moved, a third connection moves along the coil tapping off a portion of the maximum voltage available. It is this portion which drives the current through the meter (galvanic machine) and the client's tissues. It is important that

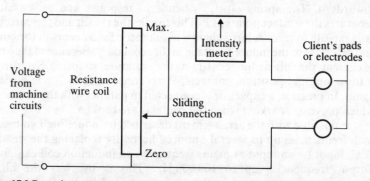

Fig. 17.9 Potentiometer connections

when the intensity controls are set to zero and the machine is switched on, no voltage is available to drive a current through the client. If this were not the case, the sudden rise in current when the machine was switched on could produce a painful stimulation in the tissues. The *potentiometer* arrangement shown in Fig. 17.9 allows controls at zero position to mean zero voltage between the pads.

Galvanic machine circuit

In Fig. 17.10 are gathered together the various circuit components likely to be found inside a galvanic machine. The components are simply represented by rectangular blocks with their name and function inscribed. The type of current passing from one stage to the next is shown between the block components.

The induction coil

This electrical device is a development of the transformer principle. It can be used to generate a high frequency, high voltage A.C. supply from a steady D.C. primary input, and this is how it is illustrated in Fig. 17.11. It consists of two coils wound on a common core, which may take the form of a bundle of iron wires. The primary coil has a small number of turns of insulated thick copper wire but the secondary is made from a very large number of turns of very thin insulated copper wire, and it is this difference in the number of turns which gives the high induced voltage (several thousand volts) in the secondary.

As we saw when discussing electromagnetic induction, a changing magnetic field strength is required to induce a voltage in the secondary. This will not be achieved by passing a steady direct current through the primary so the *make-and-break* shown in Fig. 17.11 is included in the primary circuit. When the D.C. supply is first switched on the core is magnetised and this causes the soft-iron armature, A, to be attracted towards it. The spring strip, S, bends in response and as a result separates the contact points at P. This breaks the circuit and the current falls rapidly to zero. A large change in magnetic field occurs in the core and gives rise to the induced voltage in the secondary. Because of the loss of current, the core no longer attracts the armature, so spring, S, returns it to its original position, contacts, P, reconnect and the cycle begins again. In practice, a capacitor is connected in parallel with the contacts which prevents sparking when the contacts are broken.

It is possible with the arrangement described to induce high voltages with frequencies up to several hundred hertz. By replacing the steady D.C. input by an input at mains frequency, an induction coil can give output frequencies up to 100 000 Hz. This is the way the high frequencies are generated in the equipment used by the therapist to

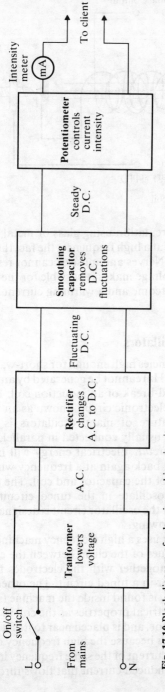

Intensity meter

mA

To client

Potentiometer
controls
current
intensity

Steady D.C.

Smoothing capacitor
removes
D.C.
fluctuations

Fluctuating D.C.

Rectifier
changes
A.C. to D.C.

A.C.

Tranformer
lowers
voltage

On/off switch

From mains

L

N

Fig. 17.10 Block diagram of galvanic machine circuit

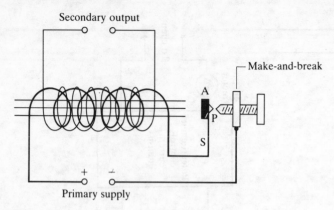

Fig. 17.11 The induction coil

stimulate the skin circulation using glass or metal electrodes. Because the induced supply is at a high frequency, the fact that the voltage is very high is not harmful. Nerves and muscles cannot respond to such rapid changes. The high voltage makes it possible for the electrical resistance of the skin to be overcome and a warming current to flow.

High frequency oscillators

Currents with frequencies high enough for short-wave diathermy (often as high as 27 000 000 Hz) cannot be generated by any mechanical device such as the make-and-break of an induction coil. Instead the currents are produced by an electronic circuit known as an *oscillator*.

An important feature of many oscillators is the presence of a capacitor and a coil, usually connected in parallel, in an arrangement known as a *tuned circuit*. Electrical energy will be transferred from capacitor to coil and back again at a frequency which depends on the electrical properties of the capacitor and coil. The energy is carried by the currents which oscillate in the tuned circuit at this particular frequency. The rest of the oscillator circuit is designed to keep these high frequency currents flowing.

When the therapist uses a high frequency machine such as those used for epilation, the tissues of the client between the electrodes which are applied to the skin, together with the electrodes themselves, become effectively a capacitor in a tuned circuit. The other component of the tuned circuit, the coil, is found inside the machine (see Fig. 17.12). This coil has the same electrical properties as the coil in the tuned circuit of the machine's oscillator, and is placed near to it. The coils are described as being *resonant coils* because the high frequency current in one (A in Fig. 17.12) induces a current of the same frequency in the other (B in Fig. 17.12), and it is this induced current that flows through the client.

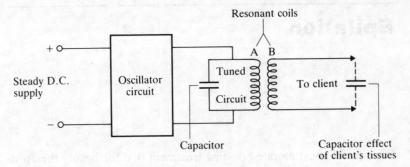

Fig. 17.12 High frequency machine circuit

Just as galvanic and faradic machines require a circuit to convert mains A.C. to steady D.C. for their power supply, so also will the oscillator circuit in a high frequency machine, as shown in Fig. 17.12.

Questions

1. What advantage, or advantages, has an electromagnet over a permanent bar magnet? What is the effect of connecting an electromagnet to a low frequency A.C. supply?
2. Select, giving reasons, a suitable material for use as (a) transformer coil wire, (b) potentiometer coil wire and (c) the yoke of a transformer.
3. In a galvanic machine what is the function of (a) the transformer, (b) the rectifier and (c) the smoothing capacitor?
4. A variable resistance coil in series with the meter would act as an intensity controller in a salon machine. Explain why this is not used by comparing it with a potentiometer circuit.
5. What is meant by the terms (a) vibrating armature, (b) electro-magnetic induction and (c) full-wave rectified current?
6. Explain why (a) the high voltage output from an induction coil is *not* harmful when applied to the skin, and (b) frequencies suitable for short-wave diathermy *cannot* be generated by an induction coil.

Chapter 18

Epilation

Perhaps the most morale-boosting treatment that the beauty therapist can give to female clients is the removal of unwanted terminal hair. This growth, which society regards as a symbol of masculinity, can be removed by three different methods and the scientific basis of these is the subject of this chapter. If the root of the hair is removed, the treatment is known as *epilation*, but if only the part of the hair showing above the skin goes and the root remains intact, the treatment is called *depilation*. It is clear that epilation will have a more permanent effect than depilation.

The hair in its follicle

In epilation we are concerned with the type of hair known as *terminal hair* which occurs as a projection from the skin on certain parts of the body surface including the scalp, face, under the arms, legs and in the groin. Each hair grows from a tiny pit, or *follicle,* in the skin which reaches downwards into the dermis (see Fig. 18.1)

The portion of the hair seen above the skin surface is called the hair shaft and the portion in the follicle is the hair root. At the base of the hair root is a small swelling known as the hair bulb which makes contact with the dermal papilla where the blood vessels occur. Nutrients are transported to the papilla and these are supplied to the cells in the root of the hair which divide, thus causing the hair to project further out of the follicle. As cells move away from the hair bulb due to this cell division, changes occur in their structure causing them to lose their nuclei and other features characteristic of a living cell. The proteinaceous material of the cell is gradually converted to keratin and, as a result, there are no living cells in the hair shaft. It consists of keratin in various forms together with the pigment granules that are responsible for hair colour. These granules are manufactured by melanocyte cells in the hair root. Three layers are distinguished in the shaft, these being:

1. The outer transparent cuticle.
2. The cortex which carries the pigment and accounts for the majority of the hair thickness.
3. The inner medulla.

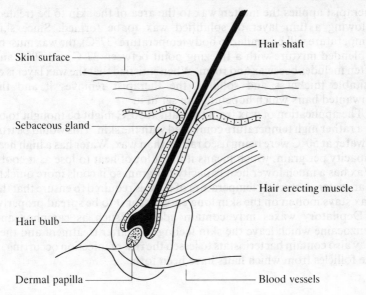

Labels on figure:
- Skin surface
- Hair shaft
- Sebaceous gland
- Hair erecting muscle
- Hair bulb
- Dermal papilla
- Blood vessels

Fig. 18.1 Section through a hair follicle

Hair growth

During the growth period of an individual hair the length increase per day varies according to which part of the body the hair occurs and also with the age of the person. The average rate of growth is 0·35 mm per day or about 1 cm per month. Other factors such as illness and malnutrition can also affect this value. An individual hair grows to a certain length, again depending on where it occurs, and then undergoes a rest period. It then becomes detached from the papilla and is eventually forced out of the follicle by a new hair growing in its place. In any part of the human skin which produces terminal hair there will always be hairs growing, hairs resting and hairs easily removable from the follicle.

Use of wax

The simplest method of removing unwanted hair from a technical viewpoint is to mechanically pull the hairs out of their follicles. Individual plucking, such as may be used with the eyebrows, is a slow process and for some areas of the body a greater removal rate can be achieved with the use of *depilatory wax.*

Salons often use this technique on the legs. A thermostatically controlled and electrically heated wax bath converts the solid wax to liquid and then holds it at a pre-set temperature (about 50°C). The therapist applies the molten wax to the area of the skin to be treated, allowing a thin layer of solidified wax to be formed. Since skin temperature will be similar to body temperature (37°C), the wax must be a blended mixture with a freezing point between 37°C and 50°C and often includes beeswax and rosin. When satisfied that the wax layer is of suitable thickness and solidity, the therapist removes it and the unwanted hairs which hopefully are set in it.

The application of wax from the bath at 50°C might be thought to be at a rather high temperature compared with the skin. This would be true if water at 50°C were being used rather than wax. Water has a high heat capacity per gram, which means it has a lot of heat to lose as it cools. Wax has a much lower heat capacity per gram so it cools more quickly than water. A starting temperature of 50°C is required to ensure that the wax stays molten on the skin long enough for it to be spread properly.

Depilatory waxes may contain additives such as camphor and benzocaine which leave the skin feeling cool after treatment and they may also contain bacteriostats to lessen the risk of infection occurring in the follicles from which hairs have been torn.

Electrical methods

Two methods of epilation using an electric current are available in many salons. The older and slower method makes use of the galvanic burn effect referred to in Chapter 16. A galvanic machine is the source of current and it is connected to a fine platinum, or steel, needle of small enough diameter to enter a hair follicle and touch the hair bulb or papilla. This needle is made the cathode and becomes the active electrode. The passive anode is connected to an area of the skin in the region where epilation is taking place. A cotton-wool pad soaked in salt solution may be used under it to make good contact (see Fig. 18.2).

The alkali produced at the tip of the needle must be sufficient to decompose the protein in the bulb so that the hair may be easily lifted out of the follicle. The hydrogen bubbles produced by the same reaction may be seen emerging from the follicle, and give the therapist an indication that removal is possible. By experience with the setting of the intensity control on the machine, successful results may be achieved but the rate of removal is slow. Since it is a chemical reaction produced by an electric current that is the basis of this method, it was given the name *electrolysis,* although the term may be used incorrectly to describe the second method also.

In the second method a high frequency, or short wave, source of current is used. Leads from the machine pass into a needle which again is inserted into the follicle until it reaches the bulb and papilla. The heating effect of the current is made use of to destroy the hair root and the process is known as *diathermy.* Chemical and stimulatory effects are avoided by using a high frequency supply (see Ch. 16). This short-wave

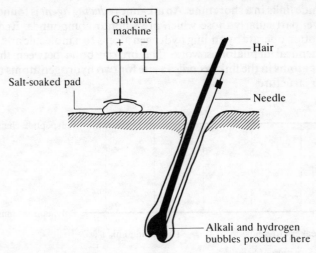

Fig. 18.2 Hair removal by electrolysis

diathermy method is quicker than true electrolysis and is consequently more popular in salons.

Chemical depilatories

Although purely chemical methods of removing unwanted hair are not normally practised in the salon, it is desirable that the therapist should understand something of their technology. Chemical depilatories must be able to remove hair without causing any noticeable skin damage. This presents a problem for the manufacturer since both hair and skin are made of the same compound, namely keratin. The desirable properties for a chemical depilatory are:

1. They should be quick-acting so as to avoid skin damage (between four and six minutes would be ideal).
2. The pH should not be too extreme.
3. They should have an acceptable smell.
4. They should not damage clothing.
5. They should be non-toxic and non-irritant.

Like all proteins, keratin is constructed from amino-acid molecules joined together in long strings and known as *polypeptide chains*. Some proteins could be chemically broken down by a reagent which separated the amino-acid molecules, but in keratin we have additional chemical cross-links joining neighbouring polypeptide chains. The strongest of these is called a *disulphide link* (see Fig. 18.3). Any compound suitable as the active ingredient of a chemical depilatory must be able to break these disulphide links in a short time. An alkaline *reducing agent* is found to be effective, particularly those which are sulphur compounds. Reducing agents often operate by adding hydrogen atoms to a molecule and this is how chemical depilatories work. The broken bond between the two sulphur atoms in the link becomes a site for two hydrogen atoms to join the hair structure.

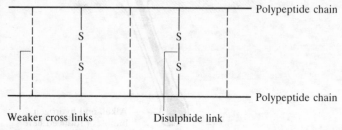

Fig. 18.3 Structure of keratin

Two compounds are now used as alternatives in depilatories. The first of these is *strontium sulphide.* Preparations containing it are quick to act, taking three to five minutes to operate, but there is a problem when using water to wash it off the skin. Hydrogen sulphide gas is generated when water is added to strontium sulphide and this has an objectionable odour. Preparations containing this ingredient are supplied with a spatula for application as would be expected, but also for the removal of the majority of the depilatory before washing. In this way the amount of gas generated is kept to a minimum.

Calcium thioglycollate, on the other hand, does not react with water adversely and so can be washed off with impunity. It is, however, slower-acting, taking five to fifteen minutes to remove. Being milder, it can be used on the face by ladies who might have an aversion to the use of a razor there. Negroid men may also find this depilatory an alternative to shaving since they may have problems with the cut ends of very curly facial hairs re-entering the skin. Care should be taken when using the product on the face and it is advisable to test a small area first for a possible adverse reaction.

Developments in the field of chemical depilatories include an examination of the possibility of using a keratin-decomposing enzyme as the active ingredient. It is hoped that such a compound would not suffer from the somewhat objectionable odour associated with the sulphur-containing reducing agents used at present.

Questions

1. What is meant by the terms (a) hair shaft, (b) hair root and (c) hair bulb? What is the function of a dermal papilla?

2. Why would you expect a depilatory wax to include (a) a mixture of waxes, (b) a skin cooling agent and (c) a bacteriostat?
3. How does short-wave diathermy differ in principle and practice from true electrolysis?
4. State the names of *two* active ingredients used in commercial chemical depilatories and discuss their mode of action and efficacy.

Chapter 19

Electromagnetic waves

In this last chapter we turn to the radiations which, when falling on our skin, may have both beneficial and harmful effects. These are the so-called electromagnetic waves which reach the Earth from the Sun and are also generated by the lamps used in the salon. We have already seen in Chapter 5 how a band of waves known as visible light enables our eyes and our brain to conjure up a picture of the world around us. In beauty therapy two other bands of waves are important and these are called infra-red and ultra-violet.

Introduction to waves

Since we cannot see an electromagnetic wave of any kind moving along it is difficult to imagine such waves in our mind. As a starting point to understanding waves we take instead those waves we have all seen on the surface of a pool of water. If we throw a stone into a calm pool it will push the surface of the water downwards at the point of impact until the molecules of the surface give way, allowing the stone to pass through. The disturbed water surface now tries to return to its horizontal shape but in doing so tends to overshoot, with the result that an up and down movement of the surface occurs for a time at the point where the stone entered.

Because the molecules in water are held together by attractive forces, this up and down motion is passed to neighbouring parts of the surface and we see this as circular crests and troughs spreading outwards on the water (see Fig. 19.1). If one stone is thrown only a few circular waves will be generated and their diameter will increase as time goes by until they reach the shore where reflections may be seen.

The water waves we are familiar with can therefore be seen to be a disturbance of the water level moving across the surface. We call the water surface the *medium* in which the waves are travelling. This leads us to a statement that is true for all waves.

A wave is a *disturbance* travelling through a *medium*.

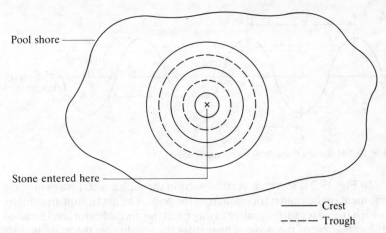

Pool shore

Stone entered here

———— Crest
— — — — Trough

Fig. 19.1 Water waves (plan view)

For example, when a therapist talks to a client she sends out sound waves which are a variation in pressure (the disturbance) travelling through the salon air (the medium).

Visible light, infra-red and ultra-violet waves do not need air, water or any other substance to travel through, for they can reach us across empty space from the Sun. It is difficult to imagine how empty space could be disturbed by waves passing through, but we do know that magnetic fields like the Earth's can reach out into space and we also know that electrons can be attracted across the vacuum inside a television tube by a high voltage anode. Considerations like this lead scientists to put these waves and others which cross empty space at the same speed into the same family and call them *electromagnetic waves*. The disturbance they cause is in the strengths of the electric and magnetic fields of the space in which they travel.

Another important property of waves which the therapist should keep in mind is their ability to carry energy from where they start to where they finish. Here the energy is used to cause some other effect, as in the following examples:

1. The energy of sea waves in winter may damage a sea wall on the coast.
2. The energy in your voice sound waves causes your client's ear-drums to vibrate.
3. The energy in visible light entering your eye will cause the chemical changes in the retina which trigger-off nervous messages to the brain.

Once a wave has given up its energy it ceases to exist. It goes no further. We must apply these ideas when considering the effect of electro-magnetic waves on the skin.

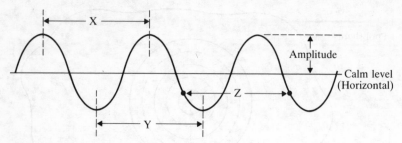

Fig. 19.2 Meaning of wavelength and amplitude

In Fig. 19.2 is shown a vertical section through a water wave at some moment in the time it travels across the pool. The maximum amount by which the water surface moves away from the normal calm level is called the *amplitude* of the wave. The greater the amplitude, the more intense the wave is. The diagram also shows three distances marked X, Y and Z. These are all equal in length and would be called the *wavelength* of the wave. X is the distance between a pair of consecutive crests, Y is the distance between a pair of consecutive troughs and Z is the distance between corresponding points on consecutive waves. Since electromagnetic waves do not have crests and troughs, we use the description of Z to give us our definition of wavelength.

The wavelength of an electromagnetic wave is the distance between any pair of corresponding points on consecutive waves. Different types of electromagnetic waves have different wavelengths and those waves used in beauty therapy have their wavelengths measured in *nanometre (nm)*. A nanometre is a very tiny length equal to one millionth part of a millimetre. At one time these wavelengths were measured in *angstrom units (AU)*. To convert a value in AU to nm we *divide by ten*.

As an alternative to wavelength, a wave may be described by quoting its *frequency*. The unit of frequency is the hertz, as used in electricity. It tells us the number of waves passing a point in the medium in one second. Short wavelength electromagnetic waves have high frequencies, and vice versa. Since the waves used in the salon have such tiny wavelengths, their frequencies will be so high that they are rarely quoted.

The electromagnetic spectrum

We saw in Chapter 5 that when light passes through a glass prism the mixture separates into its component colours and forms a pattern on a screen known as a spectrum. We call this the visible spectrum. The idea can be extended to embrace all electromagnetic waves and in Fig. 19.3 a chart is drawn showing where the different types of waves fall on a wavelength scale. This chart is known as the *electromagnetic spectrum*.

Type of wave	X-rays and gamma rays	Ultra-violet			Visible light	Infra-red		Radio
		UVC	UVB	UVA	V I B G Y O R	Short	Long	
Wave length	Short	100 nm	280 nm	315 nm 400 nm	700 nm	1400 nm	1 mm	Long
Frequency	High							Low
Description	Cold invisible rays				Visible rays	Warm invisible rays		
Skin penetration	Superficial epidermis	Deep epid.	Blood vessels of dermis	Subcutaneous tissue		Superficial epidermis		
Sun's radiation at Earth's surface								

Fig. 19.3 The electromagnetic spectrum

Certain other information is included in Fig. 19.3 to show how properties change with wavelength. One of these is the depth to which the waves penetrate the skin and it will be observed that, contrary to popular belief, ultra-violet waves are not as penetrating as short wavelength infra-red waves. The energy carried by infra-red waves is absorbed by whole molecules, especially those of water. When molecules receive energy they move about more rapidly and we notice this as a rise in temperature (see Ch. 1). Ultra-violet waves carry more energy than infra-red waves and this can cause changes in molecular structure or, in other words, chemical changes. It is these chemical changes in the skin which could be regarded as more dramatic and, perhaps, more dangerous even though they may occur in the epidermis. Beneficial melanin production and harmful skin cancer both involve chemical changes.

Infra-red waves

These waves emitted by objects at higher temperatures than their surroundings cover a very wide wavelength band of the electromagnetic spectrum, as Fig. 19.3 shows, but those at the short wavelength end of the band from 700 to 1,400 nm are the most important to the beauty therapist. They penetrate the skin to the subcutaneous tissue and here give up their energy to produce tissue heating.

True infra-red generators are sometimes found in beauty salons and they must be used with great care since they do not glow when in use although they are hot. A more common source of infra-red used in the salon is the *radiant heat lamp* (see Fig. 19.4). This is a tungsten filament lamp of about 250 W rating. A silvered reflecting surface on the inside of the bulb at the cap end directs the radiation through the glass window, which is often red. Visible light is also produced at the filament so the lamp can be seen to be operating, but the red glass will filter out some of the light at the violet end of the spectrum and hence reduce the brightness of the lamp when in use. Figure 19.3 also shows that visible light penetrates deeply into the skin and, like infra-red waves, has a warming effect on the tissues.

There are a number of applications of infra-red that take place in the salon, all making use of its heating effect. These include:

(a) relaxing muscles;
(b) relieving pain;
(c) increasing blood and lymph flow.

The therapist should make sure that the client does not receive too much heating from the lamps used or this will produce excessive sweating and may cause skin burns.

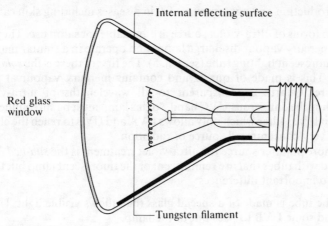

Fig. 19.4 Radiant heat lamp

Ultra-violet waves

This group of invisible waves with wavelengths shorter than violet light is divided into three bands as shown in Fig. 19.3. The bands are designated as UVA (315 to 400 nm), UVB (280 to 315 nm) and UVC (100 to 280 nm). They are all characterised by their ability to produce chemical changes in the skin. Their penetrating power diminishes as their wavelength decreases. The ultra-violet radiation that reaches the Earth's surface from the Sun does not contain UVC, as the energy from this band of waves is absorbed in the upper part of the atmosphere causing ozone to be produced from ordinary oxygen. The UVA and UVB that fall on us when we sunbathe have two beneficial effects. These are:

1. The production of a sun-tan (UVA and UVB).
2. The production of vitamin D in the skin (UVB).

UVA produces an immediate but short-lived tan by converting colourless melanin already present in the skin to a brown pigment. UVB energy increases melanin production by the melanocytes, so causing a delayed but longer-lasting tan.

The beauty salon will normally provide a service in which clients may obtain the advantages of exposure to ultra-violet waves if natural sun-bathing is not available. Such treatment may also be used to produce melanin in the skin to act as an ultra-violet absorber on a later sunny holiday. Excessive exposure to these waves either from the sun or salon lamps can cause:

(a) blisters and burning;
(b) ageing of the skin due to loss of elasticity and thickening of the stratum corneum;

(c) production and aggravation of skin diseases including skin cancer.

Two forms of ultra-violet source are available for salon use. They are both mercury vapour discharge lamps and operate in a similar manner to a fluorescent lighting tube (see Ch. 5). The first of these is the *solarium lamp*. This is made of quartz and contains mercury vapour at high pressure. Quartz is transparent to all wavelengths of ultra-violet including the dangerous UVC band, so this lamp must be surrounded by a special glass filter which only allows UVA and UVB to reach the client. It is a very concentrated source of radiation.

A more popular source for ultra-violet treatment is the *sun-bed*. This is fitted with tubes that are reminiscent of the fluorescent lamp but there are two important differences:

1. The tube is made of a special glass that allows visible light, UVA, and some UVB to pass out of the lamp.
2. The special phosphor coating converts UVC produced by the current passing through the mercury vapour, to UVA and visible light which can then emerge from the lamp.

A comparison between the fluorescent lighting tube and the sun-bed tube is illustrated in Fig. 19.5 (a), (b). The therapist should make the client aware that the action of ultra-violet waves on the eyes is quite different from that on the skin and should insist on goggles being worn.

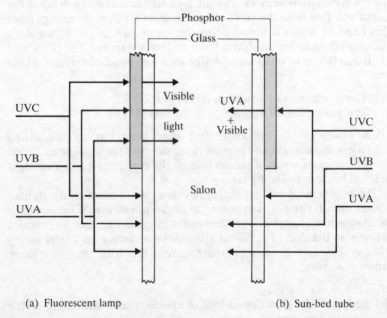

(a) Fluorescent lamp   (b) Sun-bed tube

Fig. 19.5 Action of fluorescent lamp and sun-bed tube

Although UVC is not used in the treatment of clients, it does find an application in the salon in some types of *sterilising cabinet* where its cell-destroying properties are made use of in a bactericidal manner. As with visible light, solid objects being sterilised can cast an ultra-violet 'shadow', with the result that part of their surface receives no radiation. Turning the object over halfway through the exposure time can help to eliminate this problem, but if the surface geometry is complex a completely sterile result may still not be achieved.

The inverse square law

When radiation from the Sun, a radiant heat lamp or an ultra-violet lamp falls on the skin surface it continues to bring energy to the skin surface for all the time that the skin is exposed. We use the term *intensity* in this connection and we mean the amount of radiation reaching unit area of the surface every second. If we reduce the distance between the lamp and the client's skin we would expect the intensity to increase, and the reverse to apply if we moved the lamp further away. The *inverse square law* states the relationship between distance and intensity more precisely. Figure 19.6 shows how the law arises.

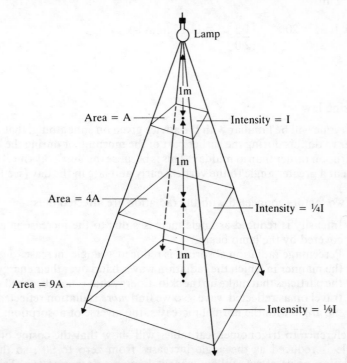

Fig. 19.6 Inverse square law for radiation

Consideration of Fig. 19.6 and a little thought will show the following trend:

Multiply distance by 2 and intensity is divided by 4 (= 2^2).
Multiply distance by 3 and intensity is divided by 9 (= 3^2).
Multiply distance by 4 and intensity is divided by 16 (= 4^2).

Such a relationship in mathematics where the increase in one factor results in the decrease of another is called an inverse relationship.

The inverse square law states that: 'The intensity of radiation at a surface depends on the inverse square of the distance from the source.'

Since salon lamps are not compact sources of radiation, the law only applies precisely if the distance from lamp to client is very much greater than the size of the lamp. A formula for calculating equivalent exposure times at different distances is:

$$\text{New time} = \text{old time} \times \left[\frac{\text{new distance}}{\text{old distance}}\right]^2$$

Example: If the exposure time with a solarium lamp 2·0 m above a client is 20 minutes, what will be the time for the same treatment with the lamp at 1·5 m?

$$\text{New time} = 20 \times \left[\frac{1·5}{2·0}\right]^2 = 11·25 \text{ minutes}$$

Cosine law

Everyone will be familiar with the advice given on sunbathing; that it is safer to do this during the earlier part of the morning or during the late afternoon rather than at midday. This is because the Sun's rays meet the skin at a greater angle to the vertical early and late in the day (see Fig. 19.7).

Two factors connected with the radiation are affected thus:

1. Intensity is reduced as angle increases due to the increase in area covered by the lamp beam.
2. Percentage radiation absorbed is reduced as angle increases due to the manner in which the radiation waves hand over their energy to the particles that make up the skin. Energy that is not absorbed will travel on as reflected waves, so we find *more* radiation reflected as the angle with the normal increases, the inverse of absorption.

A reference to trigonometrical tables will show that the cosine of an angle is reduced as the angle increases from zero to 90°, so these radiation angle effects follow what is known as a *cosine law*. Taken

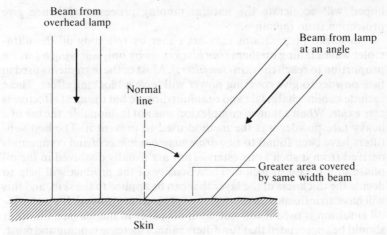

Fig. 19.7 Cosine law for radiation

together they mean that the radiation from a treatment lamp will become less effective as it meets the body surface at a large angle with the normal line drawn to the surface at that point. The therapist should consider how lamp position and body contours will determine this angle. For example, if the client is lying horizontally beneath a solarium lamp, which will be short in length compared with the length of the human body, the extremities of the body surface, though perhaps horizontal, may receive radiation at quite a large angle to the normal and, consequently, become less tanned than areas immediately below the lamp. This will mean repositioning the client after a period of treatment to bring the extremities under the lamp. Again, because of the shape of the human body, it will not be possible for all surfaces to receive radiation at right angles at the same time. If, for example, infra-red treatment is being given to the hands to improve circulation and relieve muscular pain, it will be important to get the client to rotate the hands at the wrist and move the fingers and thumbs about while under the lamp.

Sun-tan preparations

These cosmetics can be classified under three headings:

1. Sun-screen preparations which prevent some, or all, of the Sun's UVA and UVB from reaching the skin.
2. Sun-burn relief preparations which would be used after over-exposure.
3. Artificial sun-tan preparations which alone give no protection.

All these products are applied topically to the skin, but there have been developments in the use of compounds to be taken by mouth which it is hoped will accelerate the natural tanning process and hence give protection from radiation.

Sun-screen preparations may act either by reflecting all the ultra-violet waves falling on them *(sun blocks),* or by only allowing a certain proportion to reach the skin *(sun filters).* Most of the ingredients used in face powder to give covering power will have a blocking effect. These include kaolin, chalk, talc and titanium dioxide but the most effective is *zinc oxide.* When a tanned complexion was not fashionable, the use of a heavy face powder was the method used to prevent it. The best sun-filters have been found to be *para-amino benzoic acid* and compounds derived from it such as its esters. They are usually dissolved in the oil phase of a cream or lotion. The viscosity of the product will help to decide the thickness of the layer that can be applied to the skin, and this will have an influence on the degree of protection afforded. If a water-in-oil emulsion is used it will not wash off easily in the sea (see Ch. 6). It should be appreciated that sun-filters cannot increase tanning and must, by their manner of action, reduce it.

Sun-burn relief products need primarily to have a cooling action on the burnt skin. This is achieved by including a liquid to evaporate (see Ch. 1) but not to be too astringent, so the choice is often water. A bacteriostat added will help to prevent infection in the damaged skin. *Calamine lotion* has been used for this purpose for many years and it gets its name from the white calamine, or *zinc carbonate,* included in it which is deposited on the skin and provides extra protection as a sun-block.

Artificial sun-tans can be just a brown pigment included in a suitable base. The pigment is not an absorber of ultra-violet waves so it does not protect from burning. A more sophisticated product will contain a compound such as *dihydroxyacetone* which itself is not coloured but which reacts with certain of the amino-acid groupings in the keratin of the epidermis to form a brown compound. Again, the pigment formed affords no protection. Some products on the market, however, contain both a sun-filter and an artificial tanning compound.

We have referred to the ageing of the skin as one of the effects of over-exposure to ultra-violet waves. Many other skin cosmetics are now being manufactured with a sun-filtering compound added as an extra ingredient to delay this ageing effect caused by our modern practice of exposing larger areas of the skin to the outside world than was formerly the custom.

Questions

1. What is a wave? Explain the meaning of the term 'wavelength' for an electromagnetic wave. In what unit is it measured?
2. How is the energy of infra-red waves and ultra-violet waves absorbed by the skin? How does this effect their depth of penetration?

3. Describe a radiant heat lamp and explain why it is suitable for the treatments in which it is used in the salon.
4. What effects on the skin do the different bands of ultra-violet waves have? Indicate in your answer which are beneficial and which are harmful.
5. For what purpose are the following compounds used in cosmetics: (a) dihydroxyacetone; (b) para-amino benzoic acid; (c) zinc oxide?

Definitions for beauty therapists

Acid	A compound which produces hydrogen ions in water
Alcohol	A compound which reacts with an acid to form an ester
Alkali	A water-soluble base producing hydroxyl ions
Animal and vegetable oils	Mainly esters formed from glycerol and fatty acids
Anion	A negatively charged ion
Anionic detergents	Compounds whose molecules surround dirt particles with a negative charge
Antioxidants	Compounds added to cosmetics to prevent oxidation
Astringents	Substances which have a tightening effect on the skin
Atom	The smallest particle of an element. They join up to form molecules
Bactericides	Compounds which destroy harmful bacteria
Bacteriostats	Compounds which prevent bacteria from multiplying ·
Base	A compound which reacts with acids to form salts
Bloom	The property of a face powder producing a matt finish
Buffer mixture	A mixture which keeps the pH of a cosmetic stable
Cation	A positively charged ion
Cationic detergents	Compounds whose molecules surround dirt particles with a positive charge
Colloid	A compound added to a cosmetic to increase its viscosity
Denatured alcohol	Common alcohol to which another alcohol has been added
Detergent	A compound which helps water to clean

Diaphoretic	Describes a face mask which increases sweat production
Dye	A soluble coloured compound
Electrolyte	A compound which exists as ions in water
Emollients	Compounds added to cosmetics to help skin, nails and hair to retain water and so keep soft
Emulsifiers	Compounds added to emulsions to help the drops to disperse
Emulsions	Two non-miscible liquids, one of which is dispersed as tiny drops in the other
Essential oils	Plant oils which are volatile and pleasant-smelling
Ester	A compound formed when an alcohol and an acid interact
Faradic current	A current which causes stimulation of the motor nerves and muscles
Fixed oils	Non-volatile animal, vegetable or mineral oils
Galvanic current	A direct current of constant intensity
High frequency current	An alternating current whose frequency is too high to cause any nerve or muscle stimulation
Humectants	Compounds added to cosmetics to keep them moist
Humidity	The water vapour content of the atmosphere
Hydrocarbon	A compound whose molecule only contains hydrogen and carbon atoms
Hydrophilic	Describes a molecule or part-molecule which likes water
Hydrophobic	Describes a molecule, or part-molecule which dislikes water
Hygrometer	An instrument for measuring relative humidity
Ion	A charged particle
Irritant	A substance which causes allergic reactions on first being used
Lake	An insoluble combination of dye and uncoloured compound
Magnetic field	The space surrounding a magnetic device which is under its magnetic influence
Mineral oils	Oils obtained from the ground
Molecule	The smallest particle of a compound

Natural ventilation	Ventilation without the use of fans
Opacifier	A substance converting a cosmetic from transparent to opaque
Opaliser	A substance producing a pearl-like effect
Permanent hardness	A condition of tap water which cannot be changed by prolonged boiling
Phosphor	A substance which glows in ultra-violet radiation
Pigment	An insoluble coloured compound
Plasticiser	A compound added to a cosmetic to make a solid film more flexible
Polar compound	A compound whose molecule has a positive end and a negative end
Potentiometer	A device used in beauty therapy machines to control current intensity
Preservatives	Compounds added to cosmetics to prevent spoilage and possible health hazards
Radiation intensity	The amount of radiation energy reaching unit area of a surface every second
Rectifier	A device which changes A.C. to D.C.
Relative humidity	A comparison of the water vapour content of the atmosphere with that required to saturate
Salt	A compound formed when acid and base interact
Saponification	The process of soap-making
Sensitiser	A substance which causes allergic reactions on being used a second time
Sinusoidal current	The type of current supplied by the mains
Slip	The property of a powder cosmetic enabling it to be spread easily and have a smooth feel
Smoothing capacitor	A device converting fluctuating D.C. to steady D.C.
Solvent	A liquid used to dissolve solids or other liquids
Stabilisers	Compounds added to emulsions to prevent the drops from reforming a separate layer
Temporary hardness	A condition of tap water which can be removed by prolonged boiling

Transformer	A circuit component which changes the voltage of an alternating supply
True waxes	Esters formed from a fatty alcohol and a fatty acid
Tuned circuit	A circuit that allows a current of one particular frequency to flow in preference to any other
Wavelength	The distance between corresponding points on consecutive waves
Wetting agent	A compound added to a liquid cosmetic to lower its surface tension so that it can wet the skin
Unsaturated oils	Oils whose molecules can accept oxygen from the air and thus deteriorate

Chemicals used in cosmetics

Aluminium chlorhydrate	Antiperspirants
Aluminium silicate (kaolin)	Powders and face-packs (absorbent)
Butyl acetate	Solvent in nail varnish
Calcium carbonate (chalk)	Powders (absorbent and gives bloom)
Calcium thioglycollate	Depilatories
Castor oil	Lipsticks (dye solvent)
Cetyl alcohol	Creams and lotions (as oil or emulsifier)
Dihydroxyacetone	Artificial sun-tanning products
Ethanol	Astringents, perfumes, etc. (volatile solvent)
Ethyl acetate	Solvent in nail varnish and remover
Glycerol	Humectant in many products
Hexamethylene tetra-amine	Deodorants (a bactericide)
Magnesium carbonate	Powders (absorbent)
Magnesium silicate (talc)	Powders (gives slip)
Magnesium stearate	Powders (gives adherence)
Nitrocellulose	Nail varnish (film former)
Para-amino benzoic acid	Sun-filter products
Paraphenylene diamine	Hair and eyelash tints
Paratoluene diamine	Hair and eyelash tints
Polyvinyl acetate	Face masks (alternative to latex rubber)
Potassium hydroxide	Cuticle remover (alkaline)
Rice starch	Powders (gives bloom)
Silica	Powders (absorbent)
Sodium aluminium silicate	Water softener (in ion-exchanger)
Sodium hexametaphosphate	Water softener
Sodium lauryl sulphate	Shampoos and bubble bath (detergent)
Sodium phosphate	Cuticle remover (mild alkali)
Sodium sesquicarbonate	Bath crystals (water softener)
Stannic oxide	Nail polishes (abrasive)
Strontium sulphide	Depilatories
Titanium oxide	Face powders, lipsticks, etc. (white pigment)
Toluene	Solvent in nail varnish

Triethanolamine lauryl sulphate	Shampoos and bubble bath (detergent)
Zinc carbonate	Calamine lotion (dries white)
Zinc oxide	Face powders, sun-blocks, etc. (good reflector)
Zinc stearate	Powders (gives adherence)

Further reading

Harry, R. G., *Cosmeticology* (Revised by J. B. Wilkinson). George Godwin Ltd.
Hibbott, H. W., *Handbook of Cosmetic Science.* Pergamon Press.
Sinclair, R., *Essential Oils.* Unilever.
Young, A., *Practical Cosmetic Science.* Mills & Boon.
Scott, P. M. *Electrotherapy and Actinotherapy.* Baillière Tindall.

Index